Teacher **Works**
by teachers for teachers

D1298746

a handbook for

Mathematics

teachers in
primary schools

Mrs Juliana Ng Chye Huat
Nan Hua Primary School
Fellow of Teachers' Network, MOE (2000-2001)

Mrs Lim Kian Huat
Principal, Yangzhen Primary School

Marshall Cavendish
Education

TEACHERS' NETWORK
Growing Together

© 2001 Times Media Private Limited
© 2003 Marshall Cavendish International (Singapore) Private Limited

Published by Marshall Cavendish Education
A member of Times Publishing Limited
Times Centre, 1 New Industrial Road, Singapore 536196
Customer Service Hotline: (65) 6213 9106
E-mail: fps@sg.marshallcaveeendish.com
Website: www.marshallcavendish.com/education/sg

First published 2001
Reprinted 2001
Second impression 2005
Reprinted 2006

ISBN 981-01-5905-6
ISBN 978-981-01-5905-4

Cover design by: Lynnica Lee

Printed in Singapore by C.O.S. Printers Pte Ltd

Foreword

In October 1994, 14,500 nine-year-old and 8,500 thirteen-year-old students in Singapore sat for tests in Mathematics and Science along with half a million students from 44 other countries. This was the Third International Mathematics and Science Study (TIMSS) conducted by the International Association for the Evaluation of Educational Achievements (IEA). The performance of our students was remarkable. Not only did we take the top spot in Mathematics for both age groups, almost 40% of our 9 year olds were placed in the top 10% of the entire study. Our Primary 3 students obtained correct answers to 62% of the questions compared to the international average of 47%. Similarly, our Primary 4 students obtained correct answers to 76% of the questions compared to the international average of 59%.

Why did Singapore do so well in this major international study? While I am sure that it is not because our students are more intelligent, it is almost impossible to identify all the factors contributing to this good performance. Nevertheless, I am certain that two of the factors are the way Mathematics is taught in Singapore and the people who teach it.

This book addresses both these factors. The authors are very experienced teachers of Mathematics. Mrs Juliana Ng was the recipient of the prestigious President's Award for Teachers and Mrs Lim Kian Huat is an Associate of the Teachers' Network. Together, they generously share how they teach the more difficult topics in the syllabus. They have also included, through their wealth of experience, pointers in Mathematics problem solving, item-construction in assessments as well as IT skills in Mathematics. As teachers, the authors are able to write in a style that speaks directly to the teachers.

I am confident that teachers will find this book relevant and helpful and the Teachers' Network looks forward to more of such books from other experienced teachers within our fraternity.

Nicholas Tang
Deputy Director
Teachers' Network

Preface

The aim of this handbook is to provide Primary Mathematics teachers, in particular new teachers, with ideas and suggestions that they can apply in the teaching and learning of Mathematics in the classroom.

The areas covered include:

- Heuristics for problem-solving

- Tips for teaching

- Enrichment activities

- Assessment in Mathematics

- IT in Mathematics

The information provided in this handbook is by no means exhaustive. It is hoped that innovative teachers will exercise discretion in adopting and modifying the suggested strategies and activities to meet the needs of their pupils.

Contents

for Heuristics Problem-Solving

The term 'heuristic' was made popular by George Polya in his book, How to Solve It in 1945. When used as a noun, the term 'heuristic' basically means "a general suggestion of what you can do when solving unfamiliar problems." In other words, heuristics are problem-solving ideas. Heuristic also means "serving to discover". Teaching heuristics for problem-solving in Mathematics is analogous to the teaching of process skills for investigation in Science.

Framework of the Mathematics Curriculum in Singapore

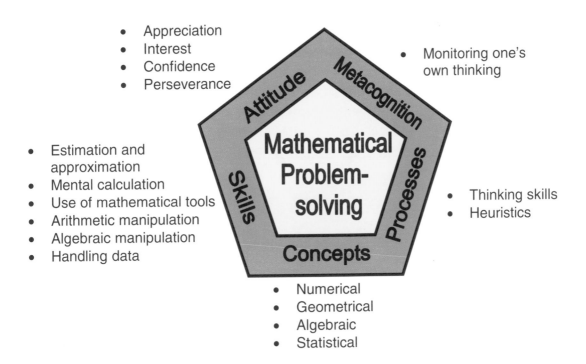

- Appreciation
- Interest
- Confidence
- Perseverance

- Monitoring one's own thinking

- Estimation and approximation
- Mental calculation
- Use of mathematical tools
- Arithmetic manipulation
- Algebraic manipulation
- Handling data

- Thinking skills
- Heuristics

- Numerical
- Geometrical
- Algebraic
- Statistical

It can be seen that the crux of our mathematics curriculum is problem-solving.

What is problem-solving?

George Polya, an eminent mathematician defines it as an act to:

1. find a way where none is known;
2. find a way out of difficulty;
3. find a way around an obstacle;
4. attain a desired end that is not immediately attainable by direct means.

What is a problem?

- A problem is an inability to proceed directly to a solution despite an awareness of the situation and an interest in resolving it.
- The following are examples of different types of problems:
  - A word problem
  - A problem in symbolic form
  - A non-routine or unfamiliar problem (as in puzzles or logic problems)
  - A real world problem
  - An investigative problem

Why teach problem-solving skills?

They
- help pupils deal with problems creatively and effectively.
- stimulate pupils and help develop thinking skills and problem-solving strategies in both new and unfamiliar situations.
- develop, reinforce, enhance and extend mathematical concepts and skills in pupils.
- develop a sense of inquiry in pupils.
- help pupils engage in imaginative and creative work arising from mathematical ideas.

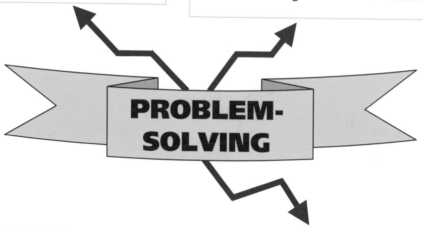

PROBLEM-SOLVING

How can we improve problem-solving skills?

- Begin with simple problems.
- Include open-ended problems and mathematical investigation tasks.
- Use as many strategies as possible.
- Seek similarities between thinking skills and problem-solving strategies.
- Provide opportunities to formulate problems.
- Use modelling to explicate the thinking processes.
- Provide time for reflection and clarification of mathematical ideas and relationships.
- Allow for oral expression to reinforce conceptualisation and development of critical thinking habits.

Problem-solving is an integral part of life.

STEPS FOR PROBLEM-SOLVING: Polya's Model

Step 1.   Understanding the problem
Step 2.   Devising a plan
Step 3.   Carrying out the plan
Step 4.   Reflecting

Step 1. Understanding the problem

- **Look for information given**
Discuss the facts and key words with pupils. Are important facts left out? Is there any redundant information?

- **Visualise the information**
Ask questions to help pupils form a mental picture of the problem. Encourage them to predict the answer.

- **Organise the information**
Through systematic questioning, help pupils restate facts. Prioritise information to be used.

- **Connect the information**
Highlight to pupils similar problems they had solved before. Ask: Which part of the information gives you a clue? What is the significance of highlighted words and numbers? Connect all information and help pupils proceed to 'Devising a plan'.

Step 2. Devising a plan

- **Select the strategy**
Leave pupils to choose a strategy to solve the problem. More than one strategy may be adopted.

- **Attempt common heuristics**
Advise pupils to attempt some of the common heuristics taught in solving mathematical problems.

Step 3. Carrying out the plan

- Pupils can start penning the strategy. Speed is not an essential element. The time taken will eventually decrease when pupils have enough practice trying out different strategies and thinking skills.
- If pupils are unsuccessful in any attempts, they can revise and modify the plan or think of a new plan.
- Bring to their attention that each plan can be carried out by using computational skills, geometrical skills and logical reasoning.

Step 4. Reflecting

- **Checking the solution**
  - Have pupils checked their calculations?
  - Are the workings clearly shown?
  - Are all relevant data provided correctly used?
  - Are given conditions of the problem accounted for?
  - Does the answer make sense?

- **Improving on the method used**
  - Is there a need to simplify the method for clarity?
  - Did pupils compare their solutions as a means of exchanging ideas?

- **Seeking alternative solutions**
  - Would alternative solutions take a shorter time to compute?
  - Would alternative solutions be less tedious to compute?
  - Is there a need for alternative solutions?
  - Has the class decided on the most superior method?

- **Extending the method to other problems**
  - Can the method be applied to other problems?

COMMONLY USED HEURISTICS

draw a diagram/model

- translate words or information into pictorial representations
- suitable for pupils who need to see to understand
- very popular method for primary school pupils

make a systematic list/tabulation

- organise, present or generate information/data in a systematic manner
- used in conjunction with the 'look for patterns' by accounting for all possibilities systematically

use before-after concept

- list information given before and after the action
- compare the information to find the unknown

guess and check

- also known as 'trial and error'
- very useful for simple problems
- systematic listing helps to narrow down to the correct guess in the shortest time possible

look for patterns

- involves active search rather than passive observation
- possible if data is provided
- involves a sequence of figures or numbers
- generalisation is needed
- information can be expressed/ viewed in an organised manner (eg. table format)

COMMONLY USED HEURISTICS

act it out

- especially useful for young pupils who enact the situation to realise the solution

eliminate options

- often applied when some of the options given are obviously NOT the answers.
- help pupils to focus on what may be possible

work backwards

- useful when the final result has already been given
- often applied in real life problems
  (eg. budgets are often made by working backwards from how much money is needed.)
  (eg. accident-investigators need to work backwards from the end results to see what had actually transpired.)

restate the problem in another way

- helps to clarify and organise thoughts

simplify the problem

- change the form of the problem so that it becomes more understandable
- usually not used by itself per se
- reword/reduce very large numbers by way of factors or multiples
- separate the problem into sub-problems to be solved individually or in sequence

make suppositions

- using simulated numbers to make problem-solving situation real

6

THINKING SKILLS

CLASSIFYING

Using relevant attributes to sort, organise and group information

COMPARING

Using common attributes to identify similarities and discrepancies across numerous sets of information

SEQUENCING

Placing items in a hierarchical order according to a quantifiable value

ANALYSING PARTS AND WHOLE

Recognising and articulating the parts that together constitute a whole

IDENTIFYING PATTERNS AND RELATIONSHIPS

Recognising the specific variations between two or more attributes in a relationship that yields a reliable or repeated scheme

INDUCTION

Drawing a general conclusion from clues gathered (from specific to general)

DEDUCTION

Inferring various specific situations or examples from given generalisations (from general to specific)

SPATIAL VISUALISATION

Visualising a situation or an object and mentally manipulating various alternatives for solving a problem related to a situation or object without benefit of concrete manipulatives.

(Taken from the Primary Mathematics Syllabus for 2001)

PROBLEM SOLVING HEURISTICS
for NON-ROUTINE PROBLEMS

Example 1

The figure below is made up of 9 identical isosceles triangles.
How many parallelograms of any size can you find in the figure?

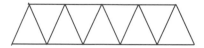

Action by the teacher:

- *Get pupils to note the phrase "parallelograms of any size".*
- *Get them to define and identify properties of isosceles triangles and parallelograms.*
- *Help them to visualise why only even numbers of isosceles triangles can form parallelograms.*
- *Gather suggestions from the class on devising a plan.*
- *Emphasise the importance of drawing diagrams as one of the methods used in solving problems of this nature.*
- *Start by drawing diagrams of parallelograms of different sizes that can be extracted from the figure.*
- *Tabulate the diagrams systematically for easy interpretation.*
- *Remind pupils to check their solutions.*

Problem-solving Heuristics : Use diagrams and make a systematic list
Thinking Skill   : Spatial visualisation

Parallelogram	Quantity
	4
	3
	2
	1

Parallelogram	Quantity
	4
	3
	2
	1

Hence, there are 20 parallelograms.

Extension: How many trapeziums of any size are there in the figure?

Example 2
In the multiplication sum below, A and B each represents a different digit.
Can you find what A and B represent?

```
        A   B   A
    ×           6   6
    ─────────────────
    B   1   4   A
B   1   4   A
─────────────────────
B   6   6   2   A
```

Action by the teacher:
- *Get pupils to understand that this is a multiplication sum.*
- *Get them to realise that A and B are both different single digit numbers.*
- *Give suggestions on how to look for clues.*
- *Most pupils will come out with the 'Guess and check' strategy.*
- *However, the strategy must be carried out by logical reasoning.*
- *Check the solution with the values of A and B in place.*

Problem-solving Heuristic	**: Guess and check**
Thinking Skill	**: Identifying patterns and relationships**

Clear-cut clues can be found in the thousands and tens summation columns.

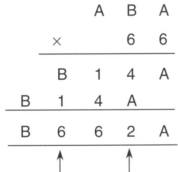

Since there is no renaming from the hundreds column, the value of B must be 5.

From this column, we can deduce that 4 + A is greater than 10 since there is a renaming over to the hundreds column. This is possible only if the value of A is 8.

Hence, the values of A and B are 8 and 5 respectively.

Example 3

At Jeya's Bookstore, magazines were sold at 90 cents per copy and comics at 60 cents per copy. Donny visited the bookstore and bought a total of 29 magazines and comics. If he spent $21 altogether, how many magazines did he buy?

Action by the teacher:
- *Ask pupils to state the problem.*
- *Ask them for the key words.*
- *Ask them to suggest how to organise the information.*
- *Encourage them to devise plans, and highlight the pros and cons of strategies used.*
- *Remind them to check their solutions.*

Method 1

P S Heuristic : Guess and check
Thinking Skill : Identifying patterns
and relationships

1st guess :
- Try 17 magazines and 12 comics
  $17 \times \$0.90 + 12 \times \$0.60 = \$22.50$ (too high)

2nd guess :
- Try 14 magazines and 15 comics
  $14 \times \$0.90 + 15 \times \$0.60 = \$21.60$ (high)

3rd guess :
- Try 11 magazines and 18 comics
  $11 \times \$0.90 + 18 \times \$0.60 = \$20.70$ (low)

From the 2nd and 3rd guesses, the correct answer is between 14 and 11 magazines.

4th guess :
- Try 12 magazines and 17 comics
  $12 \times \$0.90 + 17 \times \$0.60 = \$21$ (correct)

	1st Guess	2nd Guess	3rd Guess	4th Guess
Mag	17	14	11	12
Com	12	15	18	17
Cost	$22.50	$21.60	$20.70	$21
	(high)	(high)	(low)	(correct)

Hence, Donny bought 12 magazines from the bookstore.

Method 2

P S Heuristic : Make suppositions
Thinking Skill : Deduction

Suppose that all the reading materials bought are comics.

$29 \times \$0.60 = \$17.40$ (less than $21 by $3.60)
Difference in cost between a magazine and a comic = 30 cents

Therefore, the number of magazines bought
$= 360 \div 30$
$= 12$

Check that

$12 \times \$0.90 + 17 \times \$0.60 = \$21$ (correct)

Extension: Provide further practice by using situations involving 2 items with different values — like the number of cows and chickens, and the number of their heads and legs.

Example 4

Ali is an office boy who works in a multi-storey building where every floor is served by the lift. His routine begins when he leaves his office and takes the lift 7 floors up to Mr Singh's office. He then goes to Miss Li's office 3 floors above Mr Singh's to collect a cheque. Next, he takes the lift 14 floors down to hand the cheque to Mr Wee. After that, he takes the lift 5 floors down to the first floor (also the ground floor). On which floor is Ali's office located?

Action by the teacher:
- *Encourage pupils to draw a sketch (on paper) of the situation.*
- *Ask them to note the key words, such as, the various floors travelled.*
- *While planning, highlight why the heuristic of 'working backward' is most appropriate for such problems.*
- *In carrying out the plan, pupils have to handle things in the reverse direction.*
- *Again, remind them to check their solutions.*

Problem-solving Heuristic	**: Work backwards**
Thinking Skill	**: Identifying patterns and relationships**

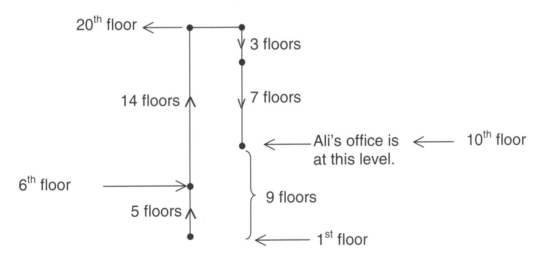

Since Ali finally dropped off at the 1st floor, work backwards using the 1st floor as our first point of reference. Reversing the original direction of flow, we backtrack
- 5 floors up to Mr Wee's office,
- 14 floors up to Miss Li's office,
- 3 floors down to Mr Singh's office and finally
- 7 floors down to Ali's office, which is located at the 10th floor.

Hence, Ali's office is on the 10th floor.

Extension: Get pupils to devise similar questions based on this experience. This will enable a better understanding of how to work out such problems.

Example 5

Alice had some books. She gave Suling half of the books plus one book. She gave Cathy half of the remaining books plus two books. If she had 6 books left after this, how many books had Alice at first?

Action by the teacher:
- *Discuss the problem with pupils.*
- *Encourage them to draw diagrams.*
- *Check their solutions.*

Problem-solving Heuristics	: Draw a model and work backwards
Thinking Skill	**: Analysing parts and whole**

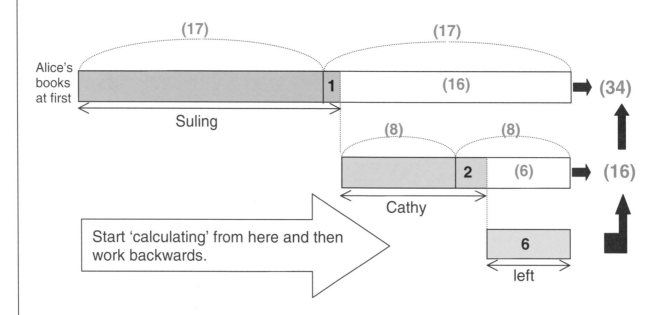

Alice had 34 books at first.

Note:
There are hardly any 'traditional' mathematics statements.
The solution is totally diagrammatic and clearly represented.
The diagram, too, is fully self-explanatory.

Example 6
How many numbers *greater than* 5 600 can you form from the following digits?
(Each digit is to be *used only once* in each number.)

| 6 | 2 | 9 | 5 |

Action by the teacher:
- *Get pupils to note key words: greater than/only once.*
- *Help them to infer, therefore, that all digits must be used.*
- *Encourage them to suggest problem-solving heuristics and thinking skills.*
- *Explain, then, why it is necessary to make a systematic list so that no relevant numbers are left out.*
- *Encourage computational skills by classification and tabulation.*
- *Remind them to check their solutions.*

Problem-solving Heuristics	**: Make a table and a systematic list**
Thinking Skill	**: Classifying**

Start by drawing a table .
Label the 'headings' systematically.

Numbers beginning with 9	Numbers beginning with 6	Numbers beginning with 5
9 652	6 952	5 962
9 625	6 925	5 926
9 562	6 592	5 692
9 526	6 529	5 629
9 265	6 295	--
9 256	6 259	--

There are 16 numbers greater than 5 600 that can be formed from the digits.

Extension: How many numbers divisible by 5 can be formed from some or all of the digits 6, 2, 9, and 5? Do not repeat the digit in the number.
(This is an entirely new problem where the number of digits to be used for each number is *not* restricted to 4.)

Example 7

Ali, Sam and Tom agreed to paint 3 rooms of the same size for Mr Yu for a sum of $144. On the day of work, Ali and Sam arrived early and completed painting 2 rooms in the morning. In the afternoon, Tom was not there yet, so they decided to paint the other room as well. When they had painted half the room, Tom turned up and together, the 3 boys finished the job. If the boys wanted to be paid according to the amount of work they did, how much should Ali get?

Action by the teacher:
- *Get the pupils to understand that each boy will be paid according to the amount of work put in.*
- *Ask them how much each boy will get for painting a room, for painting half a room or a quarter of a room*
- *Encourage the pupils to try out the problem mentally and then highlight the common mistakes likely to incur if solved mentally.*
- *Lead the pupils to devise a plan with the drawing of a 'part-whole' model in mind.*
- *Carry out the plan by proportioning the model.*
- *Check solution.*

Problem-solving Heuristic	**: Draw a model**
Thinking Skill	**: Deduction**

Rate per day for painting a room = $(144 ÷ 3) = $48

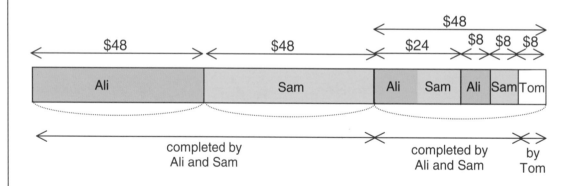

Amount of money Ali should get = $(48 + 12 + 8) = $68.

Example 8
A ball was dropped from a height of 8m. When it hit the ground, it bounced up to half the height from which it was dropped. The ball was caught when it bounced up 1m from the ground. Find the total **vertical** distance that the ball had travelled.

Action by the teacher:
- *Get the pupils to understand the problem with the help of a sketch.*
- *Get the pupils to note the key words.*
- *In devising a plan, get them to understand why it is necessary to label the diagrams they draw.*
- *Check solution.*

Problem-solving Heuristic	**: Draw a diagram**
Thinking Skill	**: Identifying patterns and relationships**

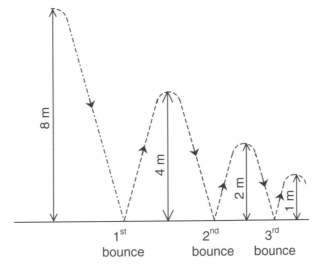

Total vertical distance travelled = (8 + 2 × 4 + 2 × 2 + 1)m = 21m

Extension: For the same problem, find the height from which the ball was dropped if the height of the third bounce was 0.8 m.

Problem-solving Heuristics	**: Draw a diagram and work backwards**
Thinking Skill	**: Identifying patterns and relationships**

Height of the 3rd bounce = 0.8m
Height of the 2nd bounce = 1.6m   *(A picture similar to the above should be drawn.)*
Height of the 1st bounce = 3.2m

Height from which the ball was dropped = 6.4m

Example 9

A pet shop owner made the following observation on the eating habits of some mice that he kept :

    2 brown mice would consume 2 kg of grains in 2 months.
    3 black mice would consume 3 kg of grains in 3 months.
    4 white mice would consume 4 kg of grains in 4 months.

At these rates, how many kg of grain would be needed altogether to feed 12 brown mice, 12 black mice and 12 white mice for a year?

Action by the teacher:
- *As pupils would probably find the problem too complex to understand, draw sketches to illustrate the situation.*
- *Get pupils to note the key words and let them engage in discussion.*
- *Get them to realise that this problem has much room to be simplified.*
- *Get them to suggest ways of restating the problem.*
- *Carry out the plan by using simple proportioning skill.*
- *Impress upon the pupils how a complex-looking problem can be easily solved when restated in a simplified way.*
- *Check solution.*

Problem-solving Heuristics	**: Restate the problem in another way or simplify the problem**
Thinking Skill	**: Deduction**

By means of proportioning, restate the problem as below. Instead of multiple months, find how much grain the mice would consume in one month.

In proportion,   2 brown mice — 1 kg of grains — 1 month,
                 3 black mice — 1 kg of grains — 1 month,
                 4 white mice — 1 kg of grains — 1 month.

      So   12 brown mice — 6 kg of grains — 1 month,
                 12 black mice — 4 kg of grains — 1 month,
                 12 white mice — 3 kg of grains — 1 month.

Therefore, in a year, 12 brown mice — 12×6 — 72 kg of grains,
    (12 months)   12 black mice — 12×4 — 48 kg of grains,
                    12 white mice — 12×3 — 36 kg of grains.

                             Total = 156 kg of grains

Or, in a month, 12 brown mice, 12 black mice and 12 white mice would consume $(6 + 4 + 3) = 13$ kg of grains.

Therefore in a year, they would consume 13 x 12 = 156 kg of grains.

Extension: What happens if the pet owner also has five grey mice that consume 5 kg of grains in 5 months?

Example 10

The figure shown on the right is a regular hexagon of side 6 cm. How many equilateral triangles of side 2 cm can be formed from the hexagon?

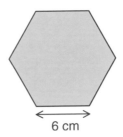

6 cm

Action by the teacher:

- *Define the term 'regular hexagon' to the class.*
- *Refresh the properties of an equilateral triangle with them.*
- *Ask the pupils how they are going to divide the hexagon into congruent equilateral triangles.*
- *Get the pupils to realise that since the equilateral triangles are congruent, they should tackle the problem by working on one equilateral triangle rather than on the whole hexagon.*
- *Get the pupils to suggest how they are going to subdivide the equilateral triangle into smaller equilateral triangles of side 2 cm.*
- *Check solution.*

Problem-solving Heuristic	**: Simplify the problem**
Thinking Skill	**: Analysing parts and whole**

Divide the hexagon into congruent equilateral triangles and then isolate one of the triangles to subdivide into smaller equilateral triangles of 2 cm sides.

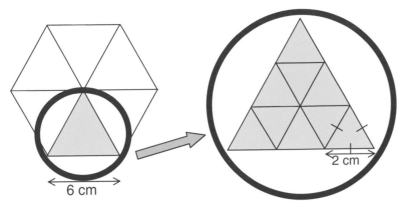

6 cm

2 cm

Draw the big equilateral triangle to scale and then subdivide it by simple construction method (accuracy is not essential).

From the figures, the required number of equilateral triangles = 6 × 9 = 54.

Extension: How many equilateral triangles of sides 1 cm, 1.5 cm or 3 cm can be obtained from the hexagon?

Example 11

How many squares, of any size, are there on a standard chessboard?

Action by the teacher:

- *Show pupils what a standard chessboard looks like.*
- *Get the pupils to understand the key phrase "squares of any size". (Most pupils will incorrectly think that there are only 64 squares on the board.)*
- *Ask pupils to name the different squares that can be found on the board.*
- *Let the pupils suggest how they are going to count the number of squares.*
- *Let the pupils know that there is a need to list the number of each square in a table systematically to avoid repetition or missing out of any squares.*
- *Check solution.*

Problem-solving Heuristic	**: Make a systematic list/tabulation**
Thinking Skills	**: Classifying and spatial visualisation**

Draw and count the number of squares of different sizes:

Size of square	No. of squares	Size of square	No. of squares
□	64		4
	49		
	36		1
	25		
	16		
	9		

There are 204 squares of different sizes on a standard chessboard.

(Example 11 cont'd ...)

Extension: How many squares, of any size, are there on:
    (a)   a 5 by 5 squares board;
    (b)   a 12 by 12 squares checkerboard.

Problem-solving Heuristic: Look for patterns

To answer the above questions without going through the process of counting squares, pupils need to identify a pattern in the total number of squares, of any size, on a 8 by 8 squares chessboard:

$$1 + 4 + 9 + 16 + 25 + 36 + 49 + 64$$
$$= 1^2 + 2^2 + 3^2 + 4^2 + 5^2 + 6^2 + 7^2 + 8^2 = 204$$

From the above, we observe a pattern and we can follow the pattern to solve the two problems:

(a)

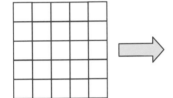

No. of squares on a 5 by 5 squares board

$$= 1^2 + 2^2 + 3^2 + 4^2 + 5^2$$
$$= 1 + 4 + 9 + 16 + 25 = 55$$

(b)

No. of squares on a 12 by 12 squares checkerboard

$$= 1^2 + 2^2 + 3^2 + 4^2 + 5^2 + 6^2 + 7^2 + 8^2 + 9^2 + 10^2 + 11^2 + 12^2$$
$$= 1 + 4 + 9 + 16 + 25 + 36 + 49 + 64 + 81 + 100 + 121 + 144$$
$$= 650$$

The examples shown above clearly demonstrate that by establishing a pattern, much time and effort can be saved in problem-solving. Moreover, the accuracy of the results obtained from observing a pattern is much higher than by mere counting of the squares.

Note: 1, 4, 9, 16 are called square numbers as they can be written as 1^2, 2^2, 3^2, 4^2.

Example 12

In a soccer tournament, each of the 7 teams (Team A to G) will play a match against each of the other 6 teams. How many matches will be played altogether?

Action by the teacher:

- *Get the pupils to point out the key words.*
- *Get the pupils to understand that there is no difference whether Team A plays against Team B or Team B plays against Team A. They will only be playing one match against each other.*
- *In devising a plan, first proceed by drawing a diagram.*
- *Get the pupils to first try out the problem by reducing the number of teams to two, then progressively increase the number of teams. This will help pupils look out for a pattern.*
- *The pupils will soon see that the permutations eventually lead to a fixed pattern.*
- *Check solution.*

Problem-solving Heuristics	**: Draw a diagram and look for a pattern**
Thinking Skill	**: Identifying patterns and relationships**

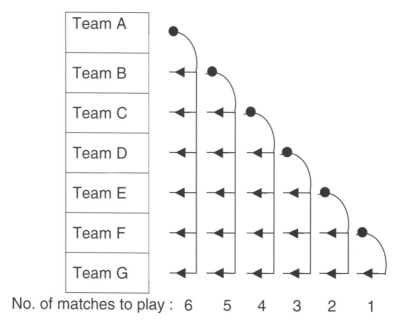

No. of matches to play : 6   5   4   3   2   1

Total number of matches in the tournament = 21

Extension: There are 10 persons at a gathering. If each person is to shake hands with every one else, how many handshakes are exchanged altogether?

Example 13

At a remote village, the only mode of communication is by word of mouth. On Monday, the village chief received a piece of news from an outsider. On Tuesday, he told it to 2 villagers. On Wednesday, each of these 2 villagers told the news to 3 other villagers. On Thursday, each of these 3 villagers who had heard the news told it to 4 other villagers. If this pattern continues, how many people in the village would have known the news by Sunday night? (Assume that none of the villagers had heard the news more than once.)

Action by the teacher:
- *Get the pupils to note the key words.*
- *Test the pupils by asking them how many villagers would have known the news by Tuesday, Wednesday and Thursday.*
- *Lead the pupils to see that the problem can be solved by a combination of strategies.*
- *Get them to draw a diagram in order to organise the information and see a pattern.*
- *Check solution.*

Problem-solving Heuristics	**: Draw a diagram and make a systematic list**
Thinking Skill	**: Identifying patterns and relationships**

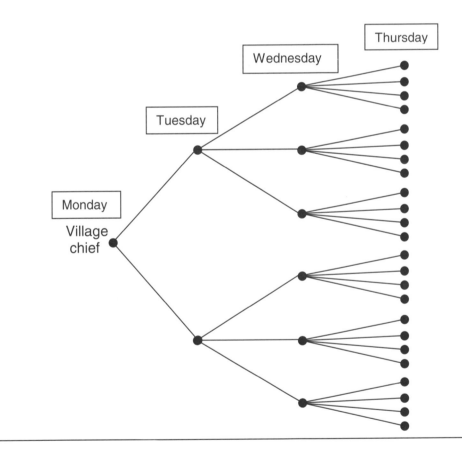

(Example 13: cont'd ...)

Tabulate the list as shown below.

Day	Number of villagers who heard the news for the first time	Total number of villagers who heard the news up to this day
Monday	1	1
Tuesday	1 x 2 = 2	3
Wednesday	2 x 3 = 6	9
Thursday	6 x 4 = 24	33
Friday	24 x 5 = 120	153
Saturday	120 x 6 = 720	873
Sunday	720 x 7 = 5040	5913

Therefore, a total of 5913 villagers heard the news by Sunday night.

Extension:

(a) The village chief received the news on Monday. On Tuesday, he told the news to 3 villagers. On Wednesday, each of these 3 villagers told the news to 3 other villagers. On Thursday, each of the villagers who had just heard the news, told it to 3 other villagers. Continuing with this pattern, how many people in the village would have heard the news by Sunday night? (Assume that none of the villagers had heard the news more than once.)

(b) The village chief received the news on Monday. After that, twice the number of villagers got to hear the news as compared to the day before. On Tuesday, 2 villagers were told of the news by the chief. On Wednesday, 4 new villagers were told of the news and on Thursday, 8 new villagers got to know of it. Continuing with this pattern, how many people in the village would have heard the news in a fortnight? (Once again, assume that none of the villagers had heard the news more than once.)

Model-Drawing

Of the many heuristics for problem-solving, model-drawing is perhaps one of the most popular for primary school pupils. This is because model-drawing:

- helps pupils visualise situations,
- creates concrete pictures from abstract situations,
- satisfies the pupils' learning through seeing and doing, and
- transforms words into recognisable pictures for young minds.

USEFULNESS OF MODEL-DRAWING

Although model-drawing is far from easy at first, it is well worth the teachers' efforts to impart this skill to pupils. When pupils become adept with model-drawing, they will be able to offer their versions of the method.

Model-drawing is ideal as a 'linking' method for problem-solving in mathematics from one level to the next. With the continuity of a common method used across the different levels, pupils can identify with at least one heuristic of problem-solving with confidence. The model-drawing method can also act as a link to algebra in the secondary schools.

STAGES OF MODEL-DRAWING

Pupils can be introduced to this method as early as Primary One.

STAGE 1: Pictorial representation

This is the introduction to the model-drawing method, or bar method.

STAGE 2: Draw pictures inside a bar

This will prepare pupils for the use of 'bars'. It also help them to be more focused and detailed in their representations.

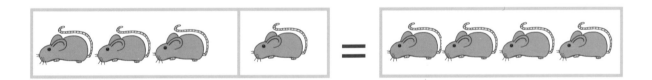

STAGE 3: Replace pictures with dots and draw arrows outside the bars

The pictures are now represented by other symbols. This will ease the drawing of complicated pictures. At this stage, the most important focus will be on the arrows drawn outside the bar.

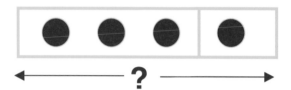

STAGE 4: Replace dots with numbers

Note the logical approximates of lengths of bars.

A bar representing a bigger value should be such that it looks bigger than a bar whose value is less. This will help in the visualisation of the solution.

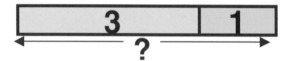

STAGE 5: Use numbers outside the bars

As problem-solving becomes more complex, put numbers outside the bars to facilitate any necessary further demarcations within the bars.

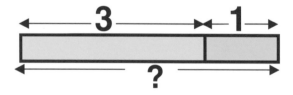

STAGE 6: Label the bars

At this stage, the pupils would have been quite comfortable with the use of models. Hence, we can teach them to label the bars appropriately.

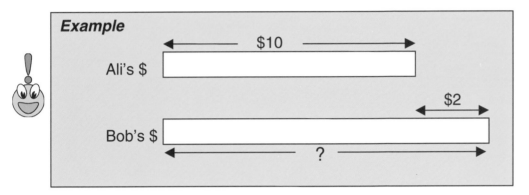

Example

HOW MODEL-DRAWING IS USED

For addition and subtraction

1. Finding the whole, given parts.

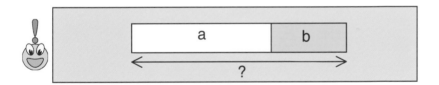

2. Finding a part, given the whole and a part.

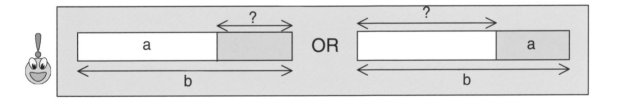

For comparison

3. Using two or more bars depending on the number of types of items involved.

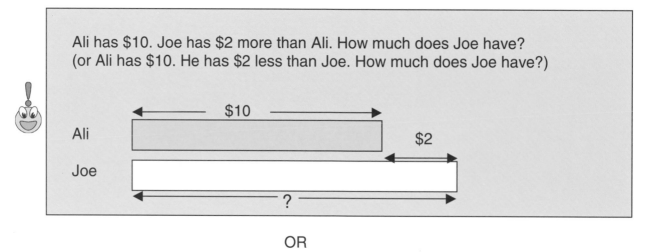

Ali has $10. Joe has $2 more than Ali. How much does Joe have?
(or Ali has $10. He has $2 less than Joe. How much does Joe have?)

OR

Joe has $2 more than Ali. If Ali has $10, how much do they have altogether?

Sometimes only one bar is needed.

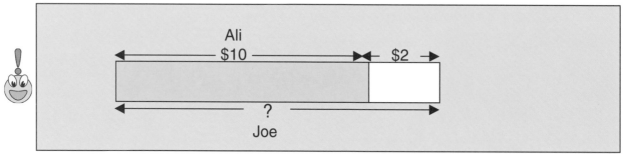

This is not wrong. But the representation is easier to perceive and understand with two bars instead of one.

Try to impress upon pupils the need to label the bars with information, such as the subject (Ali, Joe) and the numerical values. This good habit helps pupils to systematically represent the data, and promotes clarity and organisation. (Avoid a bar with no data shown.)

For multiplication or division

4.   The following are examples for comparing two sets of objects:

Mary had 24 stamps. Amy had 3 times as many as Mary.
How many stamps did Amy have?

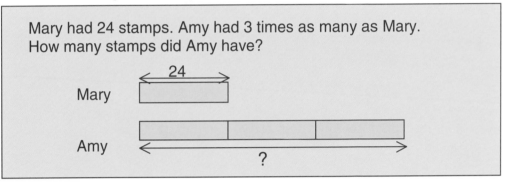

Mary had 24 stamps. She had 3 times as many as Amy.
How many stamps did Amy have?

Mary had 24 stamps. Amy had 2 stamps.
How many times as many stamps did Mary have?

Mr Lim divided his stamps into 16 sets of 4 stamps each.
How many stamps did he have?

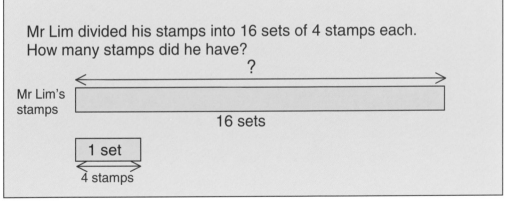

Mr Lim divided 16 stamps equally into 4 sets.
How many stamps were there in each set?

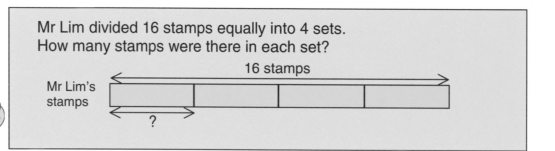

Mr Lim divided 16 stamps into sets of 4 stamps each.
How many sets were there?

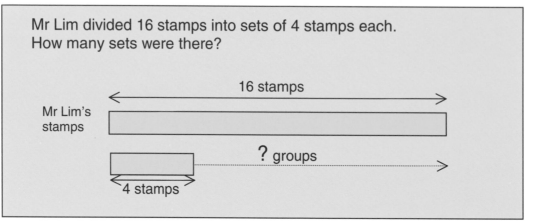

Note:

For sums involving ? times as much as ......,

Use 'Jane has **3 times as much money as** I.'
This is clear that if Jane has $15, I will have $5.

Avoid ....

'Jane has **3 times more money than** I.'
This is not clear. If Jane has $5, do I have $15 or $20?

In Singapore, it has been agreed that we would use '3 times as much as' instead of '3 times more than' for comparison purposes in the contexts stated above.

USING MODELS IN PROBLEM-SOLVING

Example 1

$\frac{2}{5}$ of a number is 12. What is the number?

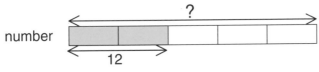

2 units ⟶ 12
1 unit ⟶ 12 ÷ 2 = 6
5 units ⟶ 6 × 5 = 30

The number is 30.

Example 2

$\frac{2}{5}$ of a number is 12. What is $\frac{7}{10}$ of that number?

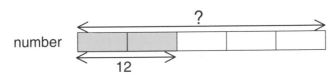

2 units ⟶ 12
1 unit ⟶ 12 ÷ 2 = 6
5 units ⟶ 6 × 5 = 30

The number is 30.

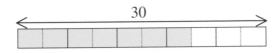

10 units ⟶ 30
1 unit ⟶ 30 ÷ 10 = 3
7 units ⟶ 3 × 7 = 21

$\frac{7}{10}$ **of the number is 21.**

Example 3

Jane's savings is $\frac{2}{3}$ of Amy's. Together their savings is $450.

How much is Jane's savings?

5 units ———→ $450
1 unit ———→ $450 ÷ 5 = $90
2 units ———→ $90 × 2 = $180

Jane's savings is $180.

Example 4

Alice and Zoe went shopping with a total of $128. After Alice spent $\frac{2}{7}$ of her money and

Zoe spent $44, they had the same amount of money left. How much money

had Zoe at first?

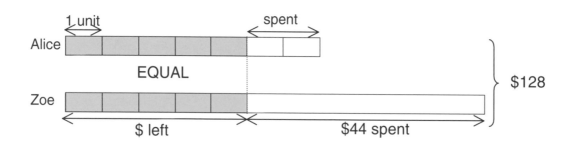

12 units ———→ $128 − $44 = $84
1 unit ———→ $84 ÷ $12 = $7
5 units ———→ $7 × $5 = $35

$35 + $44 = $79

Zoe had $79 at first.

Example 5

Suling and May went shopping with a total of $128. After Suling had spent $\frac{2}{7}$ of her money and May had spent $40, Suling found that the amount she had left was $\frac{1}{3}$ of what May had left. How much money had May at first?

$\frac{5}{7}$ of Suling's money $= \frac{1}{3}$ of the money that May had left

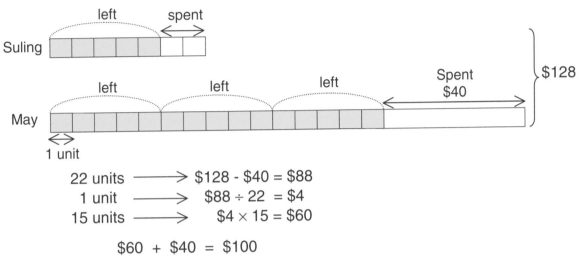

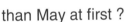

$$22 \text{ units} \longrightarrow \$128 - \$40 = \$88$$
$$1 \text{ unit} \longrightarrow \$88 \div 22 = \$4$$
$$15 \text{ units} \longrightarrow \$4 \times 15 = \$60$$

$$\$60 + \$40 = \$100$$

May had $100 at first.

Example 6

Liming and May had 192 stickers altogether. After Liming gave $\frac{1}{5}$ of his stickers to May, they had the same number of stickers. How many more stickers had Liming than May at first ?

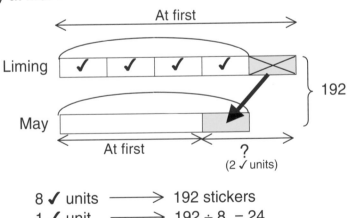

$$8 \checkmark \text{ units} \longrightarrow 192 \text{ stickers}$$
$$1 \checkmark \text{ unit} \longrightarrow 192 \div 8 = 24$$
$$2 \checkmark \text{ units} \longrightarrow 24 \times 2 = 48$$

Liming had 48 more stickers than May at first.

Example 7

Ailing's allowance is $\frac{3}{4}$ of Yenming's. Zhilong's allowance is $\frac{2}{3}$ of Ailing's. If Yenming's allowance is $48, what is Zhilong's allowance?

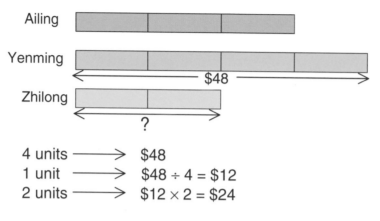

4 units $\longrightarrow$ $48
1 unit $\longrightarrow$ $48 ÷ 4 = $12
2 units $\longrightarrow$ $12 × 2 = $24

Zhilong's allowance is $24.

Example 8

The total mass of 3 ducks and 2 ducklings is 11kg. 4 ducks and 3 ducklings have a total mass of 15kg. If all the ducks have the same mass and all the ducklings have the same mass, what is the total mass of 2 ducks and 1 duckling?

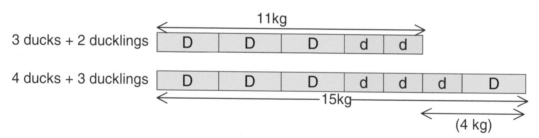

Method 1

15 – 11 = 4
Mass of 1 duck and 1 duckling is 4kg.
Mass of 3 ducks and 2 ducklings is 11kg.

11 – 4 = 7

Therefore, the total mass of 2 ducks and 1 duckling is 7kg.

Method 2

15 – 11 = 4
Mass of 1 duck and 1 duckling is 4kg.

4 × 3 = 12
Mass of 3 ducks and 3 ducklings is 12kg.

15 – 12 = 3
Therefore, the mass of 1 duck is 3kg.

4 – 3 = 1
Mass of 1 duckling is 1kg.

(2 × 3) + 1 = 7

The total mass of 2 ducks and 1 duckling is 7kg.

Example 9

A 1 000 seat multiplex is divided into 3 theatres.
There are 310 seats in Theatre 1.
Theatre 3 has 180 seats more than Theatre 2.
How many seats are there in Theatre 2?

No. of seats in Theatres 2 and 3 ⟶ 1 000 − 310 = 690

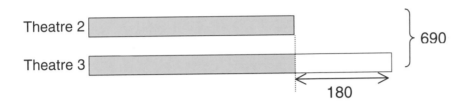

690 − 180 = 510
510 ÷ 2   = 255

There are 255 seats in Theatre 2.

Example 10

Melissa had $50. She bought a toy bear and some shampoo. The shampoo cost half
the price of the toy bear. She then spent half of what she had left on a purse. She was
left with $16.
    a) How much did the shampoo cost?
    b) How much did the toy bear cost?

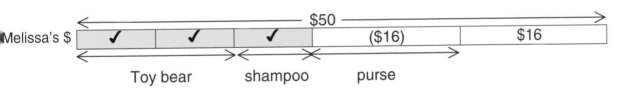

50 − 16 − 16 = 18
3 ✓ units ⟶ $18
1 ✓ unit ⟶ $6

a) The shampoo cost $6

2 x 6 = 12

b) The toy bear costs $12.

Example 11

Jean and Lucy have some beads. If Jean gives Lucy 10 of her beads, they would have the same number of beads. If Lucy gives 20 of her beads to Jean, Jean would have thrice as many beads as Lucy. How many beads did Jean and Lucy each have at first?

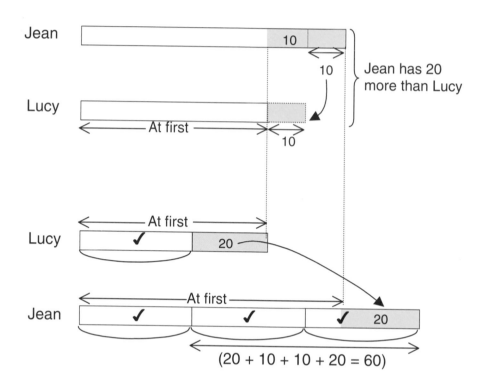

2 ✓ units ⟶ 60 beads
1 ✓ unit ⟶ 60 ÷ 2 = 30

30 + 20 = 50
Lucy had 50 beads at first.

50 + 20 = 70
Jean had 70 beads at first.

Example 12

In a class of 45, there were 4 times as many boys as girls. When some girls left for a meeting, there were then 6 times as many boys as girls. How many girls went for the meeting?

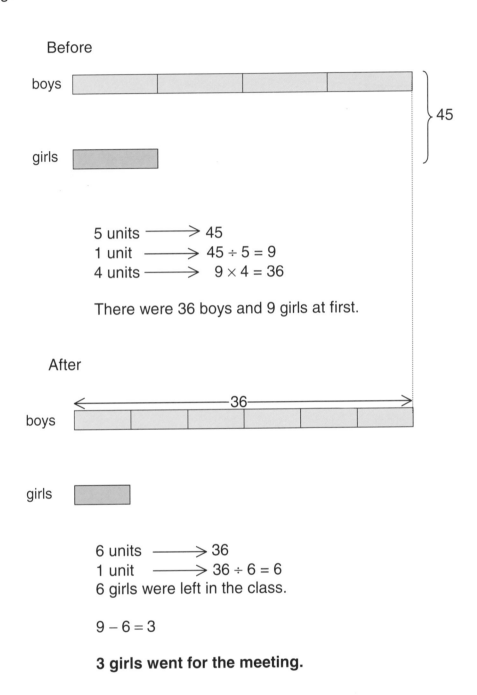

Before

boys

girls

$}$ 45

5 units $\longrightarrow$ 45
1 unit $\longrightarrow$ 45 ÷ 5 = 9
4 units $\longrightarrow$ 9 × 4 = 36

There were 36 boys and 9 girls at first.

After

boys
$\longleftarrow$————36————$\longrightarrow$

girls

6 units $\longrightarrow$ 36
1 unit $\longrightarrow$ 36 ÷ 6 = 6
6 girls were left in the class.

9 − 6 = 3

3 girls went for the meeting.

Example 13

Ann and Bill had $300 altogether. Both of them spent $70 each on a present. Ann then had 3 times as much money left as Bill had left. How much did Ann have at first?

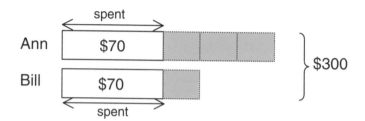

300 – 140 = 160

4 small units ⟶ $160
1 small unit ⟶ $160 ÷ 4
= $40

70 + (40 × 3) = 190

> **Note:**
> It is interesting to note that there are actually 2 types of units involved in the model: big and small. Accuracy demands that we specify which unit we are referring to when we say 4 units — $160. Wherever possible, point this out to the pupils.

Ann had $190 at first.

Example 14

In a school, there are 18 fewer male teachers than female teachers. If 45% of the teachers are male, how many teachers are there in the school?

$$45\% = \frac{9}{20} ; \qquad 55\% = \frac{11}{20}$$

Method 1 (using fractions)

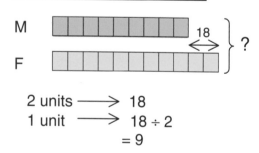

2 units ⟶ 18
1 unit ⟶ 18 ÷ 2
= 9

20 units ⟶ 9 × 20
= 180

There were 180 teachers.

Method 2

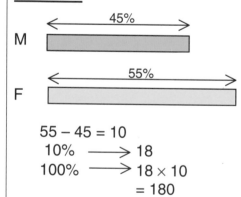

55 – 45 = 10
10% ⟶ 18
100% ⟶ 18 × 10
= 180

There were 180 teachers.

Example 15

In a stall, 60% of the soft toys were bears and the rest were monkeys. When 80 new toys were added to the collection, the number of toy bears were doubled and the number of toy monkeys was increased by 50%. How many toys were there in the stall at first?

$$60\% = \frac{3}{5} \ ; \qquad 50\% = \frac{1}{2}$$

Method 1 (using fractions)

Before:

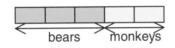

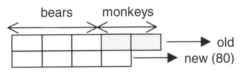

After:

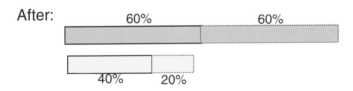

4 units $\longrightarrow$ 80
1 unit $\longrightarrow$ $80 \div 4 = 20$
5 units $\longrightarrow$ $5 \times 20 = 100$

There were 100 toys at first.

Method 2

Before:

bears   60%

monkeys   40%

?

After:

60%   60%

40%   20%

60% + 20% $\longrightarrow$ 80
80% $\longrightarrow$ 80
1% $\longrightarrow$ 1
100% $\longrightarrow$ 100

There were 100 toys at first.

Example 16

In a class of 32 pupils, 25% are boys. If some more boys join the class and the percentage of boys increases to 40%, how many boys join the class?

Method 1

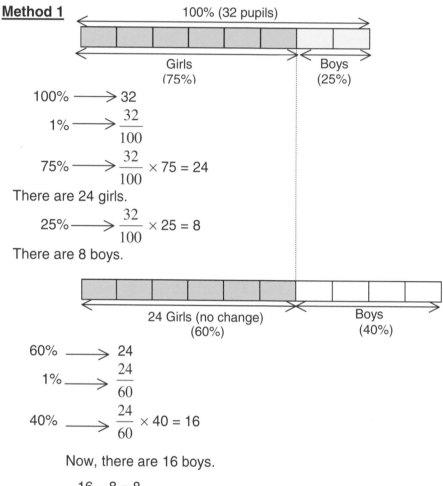

100% ⟶ 32

$$1\% \longrightarrow \frac{32}{100}$$

$$75\% \longrightarrow \frac{32}{100} \times 75 = 24$$

There are 24 girls.

$$25\% \longrightarrow \frac{32}{100} \times 25 = 8$$

There are 8 boys.

60% ⟶ 24

$$1\% \longrightarrow \frac{24}{60}$$

$$40\% \longrightarrow \frac{24}{60} \times 40 = 16$$

Now, there are 16 boys.

16 − 8 = 8

8 boys join the class.

Method 2

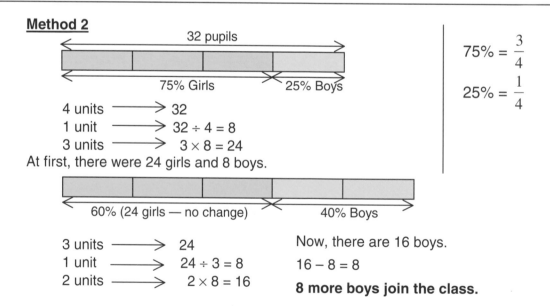

$$75\% = \frac{3}{4}$$

$$25\% = \frac{1}{4}$$

4 units ⟶ 32
1 unit ⟶ 32 ÷ 4 = 8
3 units ⟶ 3 × 8 = 24

At first, there were 24 girls and 8 boys.

3 units ⟶ 24
1 unit ⟶ 24 ÷ 3 = 8
2 units ⟶ 2 × 8 = 16

Now, there are 16 boys.

16 − 8 = 8

8 more boys join the class.

Example 17

Janet saves 20% of her monthly salary. If her salary is decreased by 5%, her savings will be decreased by $12. What is her monthly salary?

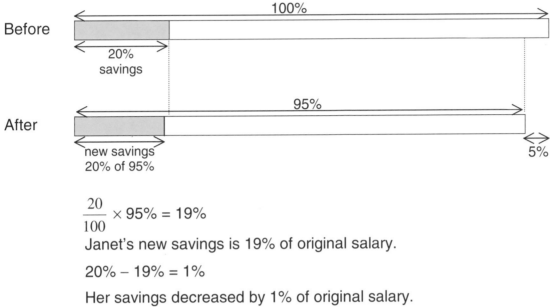

$$\frac{20}{100} \times 95\% = 19\%$$

Janet's new savings is 19% of original salary.

$$20\% - 19\% = 1\%$$

Her savings decreased by 1% of original salary.

$$1\% \longrightarrow \$12$$
$$100\% \longrightarrow \$1\ 200$$

Janet's monthly salary is $1 200.

Example 18

If Ali sells his car at a discount of 5% of the usual price, he will earn $7 000. If he sells the car at a discount of 20% of the usual price, he will lose $2 000. Find the cost price of the car.

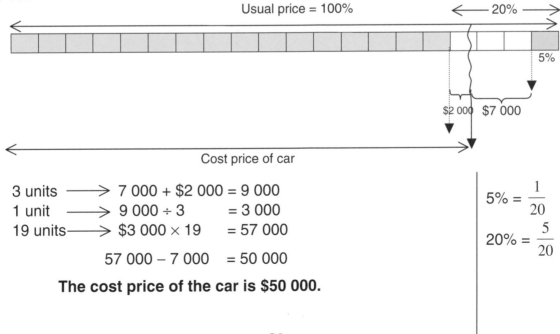

3 units $\longrightarrow$ 7 000 + $2 000 = 9 000
1 unit $\longrightarrow$ 9 000 ÷ 3 = 3 000
19 units $\longrightarrow$ $3 000 × 19 = 57 000

57 000 − 7 000 = 50 000

The cost price of the car is $50 000.

$$5\% = \frac{1}{20}$$

$$20\% = \frac{5}{20}$$

# of Teaching Some Topics

This section contains some tips to help teachers enhance their teaching strategies as well as to pre-empt pupils' misconceptions in the following topics:

- Whole numbers
- Fractions
- Decimals
- Mensuration
- Statistics
- Geometry
- Percentage

WHOLE NUMBERS

1.1 Number bonds

There are different combinations of numbers that make up a given number.

- After concepts are taught, help beginners to commit to memory the number bonds of 10 and 20.
- Have lots of oral practice on the number bonds.
- Provide hands-on activities for pupils.

Example
Pupils in their respective groups will each hold a card containing 10 squares (bond of 10) or 20 squares (bond of 20). Part of the squares should be filled with drawings.

The teacher asks: Which number and 6 will make 10? The pupil with the 4 filled squares will raise her hand and surrender her 'scored' card. This is repeated and the first group to be left without any cards is the winner.

The activity can be continued with even more cards. The 20-squared card would be used for number bonds of 20.

- Familiarise pupils with the type of format relating to number bonds.

Example

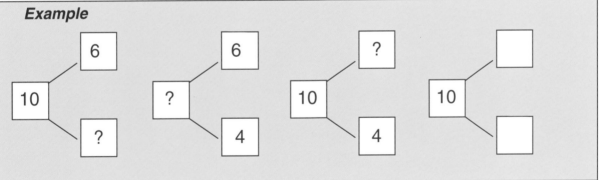

Extension : You may want to encourage pupils to try with more numbers adding up to either 10 or more at the same time.

1.2 Place Values

> The place-value concept is the basis of the base-ten system of numeration. For example, we interpret a 5-digit number in terms of ten thousands, thousands, hundreds, tens and ones. These are known as place values.

- There has been some confusion over the terms 'place value', 'stands for' and 'value of'.

- 'Stands for' and 'value of' actually represent the same thing. In this case, use numerals to represent the value.

Example
The digit '6' in 68 stands for 60.

The value of the digit '6' in 68 is 60.

- However, for 'place value', you might want to consider using words.

Example
The place value of '6' in 68 is tens.

- It is wrong to say that the 'place value' of the digit '6' in 68 is 60.

- <u>Exclude</u> sums like :

Example
2837 = ☐ thousands ☐ hundreds ☐ tens ☐ ones

Note the 's'. This practice will confuse pupils on when to write 's' and when not to. Many pupils write 2837 in words as two thousands, eight hundreds and thirty-seven which is wrong.

1.3 Cardinal/ordinal numbers

Nominal numbers mostly appear as names on objects. These numbers may code other useful information. Football jerseys have nominal numbers on them. Combinations of numbers and letters on vehicular licence tags are used for identification. For example, Room 245 is often on the second floor.

Ordinal numbers identify the location of an object in a sequence. For example, Jane is first (1st) in line. Mary is second (2nd).

Cardinal numbers are counting numbers and tell how many objects are in a set, whether we physically count the set or not. For example, Ailing has 1 cat. Jane has 5 cats.

- Familiarise pupils with the directions left and right.
- Get pupils to 'chant' the ordinal numbers – first, second, third, fourth, fifth, sixth, etc.
- Help pupils spell the ordinal numbers.
- Encourage awareness of the 'st', 'nd', 'rd' and 'th' as in 1st, 2nd, 3rd, 4th, 11th, 32nd, 33rd, etc.
- Always include the direction in the question.

Example
4th from the left

Circle the 4th skunk from the left.

(Do not assume that pupils will all start from the same direction.)

1.4 'More than'/'less than' involving box sums

- Concentrate on the words 'more than' and 'less than'.
- Give pupils lots of oral exercises.

Example
What is more than 8?
What is more than 3?
What is less than 8?
What is less than 3?

You may want to limit their answers.

- For a start, ask open-ended questions to encourage multiple answers.

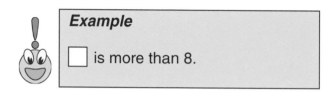

Example

☐ is more than 8.

- Let pupils give multiple answers such as 9, 15, 16, etc.
- Try with another number.
- Next, make the question more specific by asking:
  'What is 1 more than 8?' Pupils can identify answer to be 9.
- Try with other examples.
- Finally use the written form of '☐ is 1 more than 8.'
- Do the same with 'less than'.

- Do not use the sign '<' or '>'. (This is out of the syllabus!)
- Use words instead.

Example
What is more than 76?
What is 2 more than 76?
What is less than 5?
What is 2 less than 5?

- To start on the topic of comparisons, it would be good to give a set of numbers and elicit the answer from pupils.

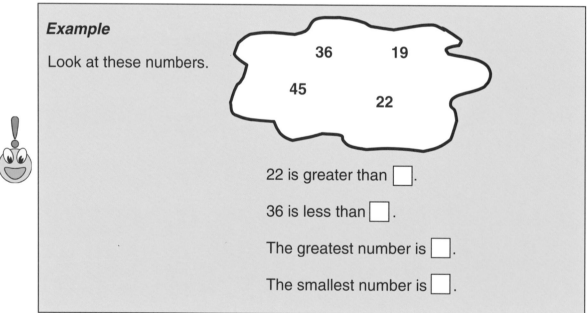

Example

Look at these numbers.

36   19

45   22

22 is greater than ☐.

36 is less than ☐.

The greatest number is ☐.

The smallest number is ☐.

1.5 'Box' sums to reinforce place value concepts and addition bonds

- Include those that emphasise place value concept:

> **Example**
>
> 700 + ☐ + 6 = 716   .... Within place value concept

- For beginners, include sums within addition bonds of 9 + 9:

> **Example**
>
> 9 + ☐ = 15
>
> 7 + ☐ = 16

- <u>Exclude</u> those that are beyond place value concept.

> **Example**
>
> 18 + ☐ = 45   .... Beyond addition bond of 9 + 9 and does not test place value concept

> **Example**
>
> 34 is 6 more than ☐.
> This is equivalent to 6 + ☐ = 34
>
> 7 less than ☐ is 16.
> This is equivalent to ☐ − 7 = 16.

Tests language

- Use these instead:

> **Example**
>
> 6 more than 34 is ☐   OR   ☐ is 6 more than 34
>
> 7 less than 16 is ☐   OR   ☐ is 7 less than 16

- Avoid sums like the following:

> **Example**
>
> What is the greatest whole number that can be placed in the box to make the statement true?
>
> $6 + \boxed{} < 50$

- This is too difficult for primary school pupils.
- Moreover, the '<' and '>' signs have been removed from the Primary Mathematics Syllabus.

> **Example**
>
> $6 \times \boxed{} = 972$ ⎫ Algebraic skills are actually involved.
>
> $52 \div \boxed{} = 13$ ⎬ Primary school pupils only learn multiplication tables up to 10×10.

- Box sums which are beyond multiplication tables of 10×10 have been removed from the Primary Mathematics syllabus.

> **Example**
>
> 60 thousands 4 tens $\div$ 4 $= \boxed{}$ thousands $\boxed{}$ hundreds $\boxed{}$ tens
> *(Are we testing place values or division concepts?)*
>
> 4 967 $= \boxed{}$ thousands $\boxed{}$ hundreds $\boxed{}$ tens $\boxed{}$ ones
>
> Write 4 967 in thousands, hundreds, tens and ones.
>
> Write the following in figures:
> 4 thousands 9 hundreds 6 tens 7 ones

- The 's' accompanying the values confuses pupils.

- Instead, include sums like the following:

> Write the following number, 4 967 in words.   OR
>
> Write "Four thousand, nine hundred and sixty-seven" in figures.

46

1.6 Number patterns

- Arouse pupils' excitement about number patterns by playing 'What's the double number?'

> **Example**
> Give a number orally and ask pupils to tell what double it is. For example, "What is fourteen?" (Double 7). When pupils have mastered such sums, proceed with any number up to 20. "What is seventeen?" (Double 8 and 1 more). Pupils love this kind of on-the-spot challenge. Give it a try.

- Start with simple number patterns.

> **Example**
>
> 1, 3, ___, 7, 9 ___, 11, ___, ___, 17, etc.

- Increase the complexity of relationships at higher levels.

> **Example**
>
> | 4 | 5 | 9 | | | | 15 | | 8 |
> |---|---|---|---|---|---|---|---|---|
> | 2 | 2 | 4 | | 5 | 7 | | 1 | |
> | 2 | 3 | 5 | 6 | | 8 | | | |
> | 4 | 6 | 20 | 42 | 25 | | 54 | 2 | 16 |
>
> Column 1 : 2 + 2 = 4
>   2 × 2 = 4
>
> Column 2 : 2 + 3 = 5
>   2 × 3 = 6
>
> Column 3 : 4 + 5 = 9
>   4 × 5 = 20
>
> Do the same for the other columns.

1.7 Order of operations

- Do not quote using the 'bodmas' rule.
- Teach pupils to always calculate from left to right, starting with brackets, then multiplication or division (whichever comes first) and finally with addition or subtraction (whichever comes first).
- Encourage pupils to underline the 'steps' they will be doing next.

Example

$$8 + 5 \times 4 \div 10 - 1$$

$$= 8 + \underline{5 \times 4} \div 10 - 1$$

$$= 8 + \underline{20 \div 10} \quad - 1$$

$$= \underline{8 + 2} \quad - 1$$

$$= \underline{10} \quad - 1$$

$$= 9$$

With time, pupils will internalise their systematic thinking. They will then no longer need to underline the steps.

- Use the ' × ' sign in front of bracket to ensure clarity of expression.

$$4 \times (6 + 8)$$

- Avoid:

  4 (6 + 8). This is not clear.

FRACTIONS

1.1 Equal parts

- It would be wise to get pupils to do paper folding for a clearer concept of equal parts. They must be well-grounded in the basic facts about 'equalness' of parts in fractions.
- Ensure that pupils understand the numerator and denominator representations.
- Help pupils to see and understand the patterns shown below:

$$\frac{1}{7} \qquad \frac{2}{7} \qquad \frac{3}{7} \qquad \frac{4}{7} \qquad \frac{5}{7}$$

The greater the numerator, the greater the value of the fraction if the denominator remains the same.

$$\frac{7}{10} \qquad \frac{7}{9} \qquad \frac{7}{8} \qquad \frac{7}{7} \qquad \frac{7}{6}$$

The greater the denominator, the smaller the value of the fraction if the numerator remains the same.

1.2 Comparison

- Start with comparing 'like fractions', i.e. fractions with the same denominators but different numerators.
- Proceed with comparing fractions with the same numerators but different denominators.
- Continue with comparing 'related fractions'.
  (Related fractions are fractions where the denominator of one fraction is a multiple of the denominator of another fraction.)

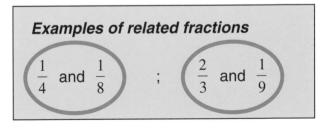

Examples of related fractions

$\frac{1}{4}$ and $\frac{1}{8}$; $\frac{2}{3}$ and $\frac{1}{9}$

- When comparing 'unlike fractions' (which include related and unrelated fractions), teach pupils to list the equivalent fractions progressively to find the relationship between them. (note: LCM – lowest common multiple, is no longer in the Primary Mathematics syllabus.)

Example

Which is bigger: $\dfrac{2}{3}$ or $\dfrac{1}{4}$?

List the equivalent fractions until the denominators are of the same value. (Always connect subsequent fractions with the first fraction in its simplest form.)

$\dfrac{2}{3}$	$\dfrac{4}{6}$	$\dfrac{6}{9}$	$\dfrac{8}{12}$	$\dfrac{10}{15}$ ....
$\dfrac{1}{4}$	$\dfrac{2}{8}$	$\dfrac{3}{12}$	....	

Now, as $\dfrac{3}{12}$ and $\dfrac{8}{12}$ have the same denominator, we need to compare only the numerators.

In this case, $\dfrac{8}{12}$ is greater than $\dfrac{3}{12}$ and hence $\dfrac{2}{3}$ is greater than $\dfrac{1}{4}$.

- Listing brings about understanding of learning of equivalent fractions. It also encourages systematic thinking.

1.3 Ordering of fractions through listing

- Teach pupils how to order fractions using the listing method.

Example

Arrange the following from the smallest to the greatest;

$$\frac{1}{4} \ ; \ \frac{4}{5} \ ; \ \frac{3}{8} \ ; \ \frac{5}{6}$$

- Start by comparing the fractions with $\frac{1}{2}$.

  (Separate them into greater than and lesser than $\frac{1}{2}$.)

Less than $\frac{1}{2}$	Greater than $\frac{1}{2}$
$\frac{1}{4}$ and $\frac{3}{8}$	$\frac{4}{5}$ and $\frac{5}{6}$

- Then list them until they come to the same denominator.
  (This is an extension and application of the concept of equivalent fractions.)

$\frac{1}{4}$, $\frac{2}{⑧}$ ......

$\frac{3}{⑧}$ ......

$\frac{4}{5}$, $\frac{8}{10}$, $\frac{12}{15}$, $\frac{16}{20}$, $\frac{20}{25}$, $\frac{24}{㉚}$,

$\frac{5}{6}$, $\frac{10}{12}$, $\frac{15}{18}$, $\frac{20}{24}$, $\frac{25}{㉚}$

Answer: $\frac{1}{4}$, $\frac{3}{8}$, $\frac{4}{5}$, $\frac{5}{6}$

1.4 Use of part-whole model method

- The part-whole model can help pupils visualise the concept of fractions.
- Start with a few <u>related fractions</u> on the same bar. (Refer to **Annex FRA-1** for practice.)

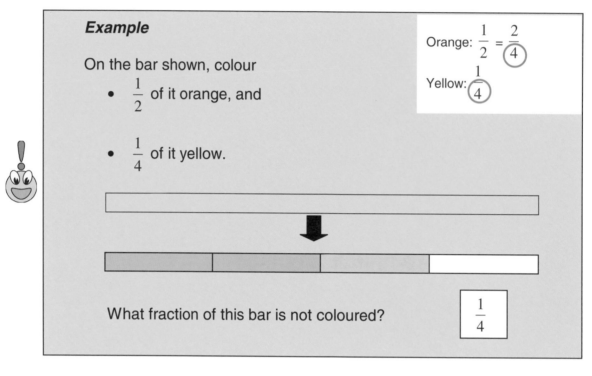

Example

On the bar shown, colour

- $\dfrac{1}{2}$ of it orange, and

- $\dfrac{1}{4}$ of it yellow.

Orange: $\dfrac{1}{2} = \dfrac{2}{\boxed{4}}$

Yellow: $\dfrac{1}{\boxed{4}}$

What fraction of this bar is not coloured?

$\boxed{\dfrac{1}{4}}$

- Then involve a few unlike (but related) fractions.
  ($\dfrac{1}{3}$ and $\dfrac{2}{9}$ are related fractions.)

Example

Andy had some stickers. He gave $\dfrac{1}{3}$ of them to Ben, $\dfrac{2}{9}$ of them to Raju and $\dfrac{1}{3}$ of them to Dennis. He had 6 stickers left. How many stickers had he at first?

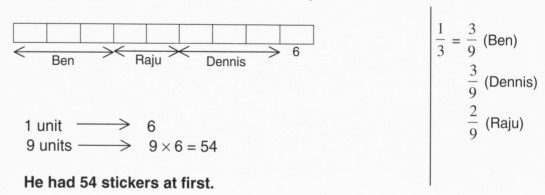

$\dfrac{1}{3} = \dfrac{3}{9}$ (Ben)

$\dfrac{3}{9}$ (Dennis)

$\dfrac{2}{9}$ (Raju)

1 unit $\longrightarrow$ 6

9 units $\longrightarrow$ $9 \times 6 = 54$

He had 54 stickers at first.

- Continue with <u>unrelated fractions</u> on the same bar.

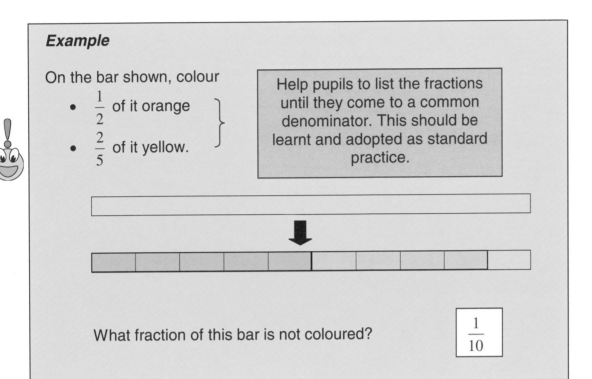

Example

On the bar shown, colour

- $\dfrac{1}{2}$ of it orange

- $\dfrac{2}{5}$ of it yellow.

Help pupils to list the fractions until they come to a common denominator. This should be learnt and adopted as standard practice.

What fraction of this bar is not coloured? $\dfrac{1}{10}$

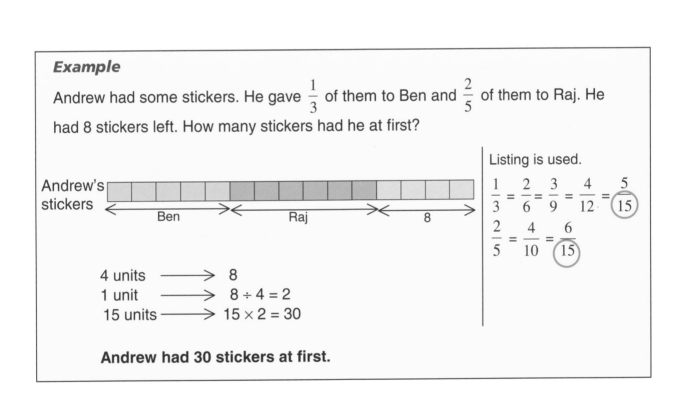

Example

Andrew had some stickers. He gave $\dfrac{1}{3}$ of them to Ben and $\dfrac{2}{5}$ of them to Raj. He had 8 stickers left. How many stickers had he at first?

Andrew's stickers

Ben   Raj   8

Listing is used.

$$\dfrac{1}{3} = \dfrac{2}{6} = \dfrac{3}{9} = \dfrac{4}{12} = \dfrac{5}{15}$$

$$\dfrac{2}{5} = \dfrac{4}{10} = \dfrac{6}{15}$$

4 units $\longrightarrow$ 8
1 unit $\longrightarrow$ 8 ÷ 4 = 2
15 units $\longrightarrow$ 15 × 2 = 30

Andrew had 30 stickers at first.

1.5 Fraction of a remainder

- You may want to start the concept of a fraction of a remainder in its simplest form (where the remainder is already in the number of units required). (Refer to **Annex FRA-2** for practice.)

Example

- Colour $\frac{2}{7}$ of the bar orange.

- Then colour $\frac{3}{5}$ <u>of the remainder</u> yellow.

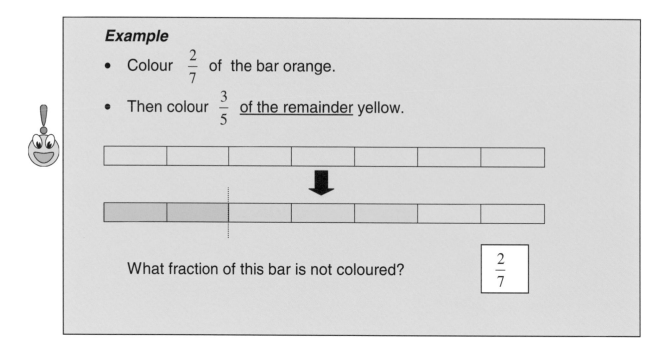

What fraction of this bar is not coloured?

$\boxed{\dfrac{2}{7}}$

Example

When Jane received her salary, she gave $\frac{4}{7}$ of it to her mother.

She then spent $\frac{2}{3}$ of the remainder on a digital camera and had $480 left.

What was her salary?

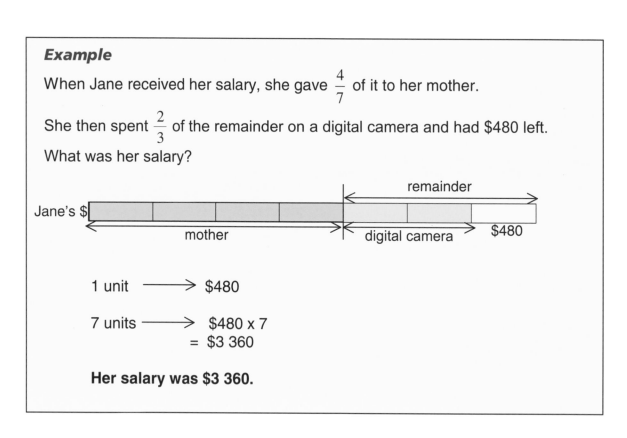

1 unit ⟶ $480

7 units ⟶ $480 x 7
= $3 360

Her salary was $3 360.

- Next, continue with the concept of fraction of a remainder where the fractions are 'not related' in terms of their denominators. (Pupils will need to re-divide the remainder into the units needed.)

Example

- Colour $\frac{1}{2}$ of the bar yellow.

- Then colour $\frac{2}{3}$ of the remainder orange.

> Note: Pupils would need to re-divide the remainder into 3 parts.

remainder

What fraction of this bar is not coloured?

$$\frac{1}{6}$$

Example

When Jane received her salary, she gave $\frac{1}{2}$ of it to her mother. After

spending $\frac{2}{5}$ of the remainder on a pair of shoes, she had $480 left.

What was her salary?

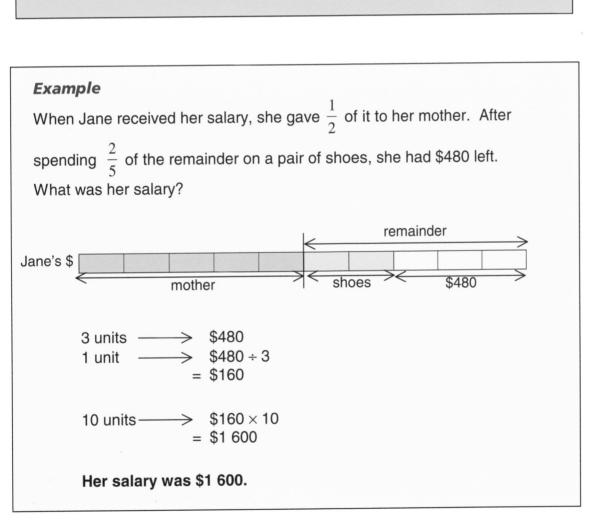

3 units   ⟶ $480

1 unit   ⟶ $480 ÷ 3

           = $160

10 units ⟶ $160 × 10

           = $1 600

Her salary was $1 600.

- Then, proceed with questions where pupils need to use the concept of equivalent fractions for the remainder.

Example

- Colour $\frac{3}{7}$ of the bar orange.

- Then colour $\frac{1}{2}$ of the remainder yellow.

Note: Pupils have to relate to the four remaining parts in terms of halves.

What fraction of this bar is not coloured?

$\boxed{\dfrac{2}{7}}$

Example

Alice used $\frac{3}{7}$ of her allowance to buy a birthday present. She then spent $\frac{1}{2}$ of the remainder to buy a skirt. The skirt cost $14 less than the birthday present.

How much was her allowance?

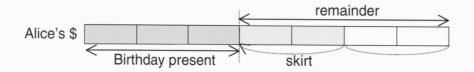

The birthday present cost 1 unit more than the skirt.

1 unit $\longrightarrow$ $14
7 units $\longrightarrow$ $14 × 7 = $98

Her allowance was $98.

56

- Finally, teach pupils to solve sums that involve the re-division of units and equivalent fractions.

Example

- Colour $\dfrac{1}{3}$ of the bar yellow.

- Then colour $\dfrac{2}{3}$ of the remainder orange.

> Note: Pupils have to relate to the two remaining parts in terms of thirds.

remainder

What fraction of this bar is not coloured?

$$\dfrac{2}{9}$$

Example

Meiling was doing a stock-check. She found that $\dfrac{3}{5}$ of the books were sold. Of the remainder, $\dfrac{2}{3}$ were still in good condition. The other 36 were in poor condition and had to be thrown away. What was the original number of books?

Split the 'remainder' units into 3 horizontal parts.
Similarly, do the same for the other parts to create equal parts.

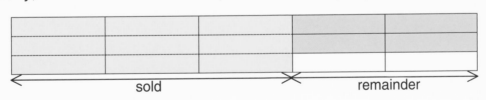

sold   remainder

2 units ⟶ 36
1 unit ⟶ 36 ÷ 2 = 18
15 units ⟶ 18 × 15 = 270

She had 270 books at first.

1.6 Multiplying a proper fraction by a whole number

- Provide hands-on activities.
  (Multiplication is the same as repeated addition.)

Example

Prepare 3 or more whole paper circles. Tear them into exact halves and display them on a magnetic board.
Demonstrate 6 times halves.

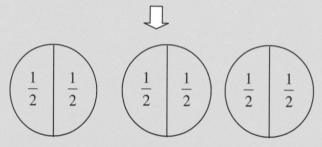

Repeated multiplication — $\frac{1}{2} + \frac{1}{2} + \frac{1}{2} + \frac{1}{2} + \frac{1}{2} + \frac{1}{2}$ — which is

$$6 \times \frac{1}{2} \quad \text{OR} \quad \frac{1}{2} \times 6 = 3 \text{ (wholes)}$$

1.7 Dividing a fraction with a whole number

- Provide actual real-life situations.

Example

John had a whole pizza. He ate half and gave the remainder to his 4 children to be shared equally.
What fraction of the whole pizza does each child get?

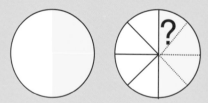

- Teach pupils to take note of the entire number of equal pieces, that is, the original parts. In fractions, all parts must be equal.

1.8 Further problems on fractions

- Pupils should use models for representation as early as possible. This will help them to visualise and understand problems on fractions better. It will be a great asset to them when they tackle more advanced 'fraction' problems in Primary Five and Six.
- Below are examples of some 'familiar' sums on the application of different concepts of fractions.

Example

$\frac{2}{5}$ of a number is 30. What is the number?

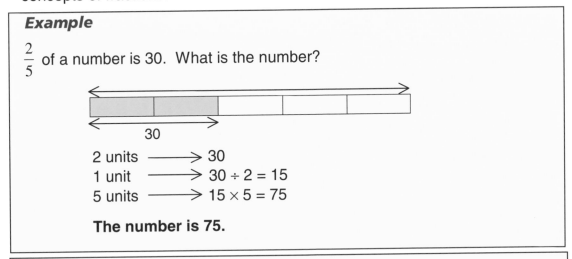

2 units ⟶ 30
1 unit ⟶ 30 ÷ 2 = 15
5 units ⟶ 15 × 5 = 75

The number is 75.

Example

There were a total of 840 boys and girls at a concert. $\frac{1}{2}$ the number of boys

is equal to $\frac{2}{3}$ the number of the girls. How many boys and how many girls were there at the concert?

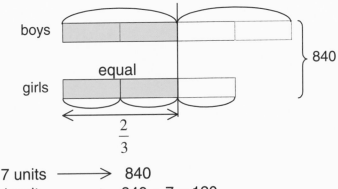

7 units ⟶ 840
1 unit ⟶ 840 ÷ 7 = 120
3 units ⟶ 120 × 3 = 360
4 units ⟶ 120 × 4 = 480

Boys ⟶ 480
Girls ⟶ 360

There were 480 boys and 360 girls.

- (Refer to **Annex FRA-3** for more similar exercises.)

Example

Amy's weight is $\frac{6}{7}$ of Bob's weight. If Amy gains 3kg and Bob loses 2kg, they will have the same weight. What is Amy's weight?

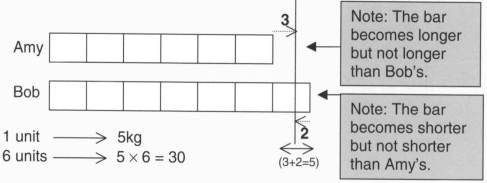

Amy

Bob

3

Note: The bar becomes longer but not longer than Bob's.

Note: The bar becomes shorter but not shorter than Amy's.

1 unit ───────> 5kg
6 units ───────> 5 × 6 = 30

2
(3+2=5)

Amy's weight is 30kg.

Note:
When the word 'if' is used, it is only a condition. Therefore, it should not reflect the actual weight as requested in the question.

Example

Of all the people interviewed, $\frac{1}{10}$ did not drink coffee or tea at all. $\frac{2}{5}$ of those interviewed drank coffee and $\frac{7}{10}$ drank tea. What was the fraction of people who drank both coffee and tea?

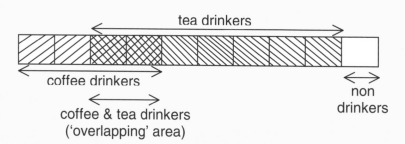

tea drinkers

coffee drinkers

coffee & tea drinkers
('overlapping' area)

non drinkers

Overlapping area = $\frac{2}{10}$ OR $\frac{1}{5}$

$\frac{1}{5}$ **of the people drank both coffee and tea.**

DECIMALS

1.1 Decimal fractions

- **Decimal fractions are used to express parts of wholes and sets divided into tenths, hundredths, thousandths and other fractional parts of tenths.**

- **The term 'decimal fractions' has been quite confusing for our pupils.**

> **Example**
> 0.56, 0.08, 0.94, etc. are all parts of a whole divided into tenths and hundredths. They are decimal fractions.

> **Example**
> $\frac{1}{3}$ is not a decimal fraction. It is not divided into tenths or hundredths.

1.2 Place values

- Connect this topic to the topic 'Money' in Primary 3. This is a good starting point to show what decimals look like.
- Teach pupils to read decimal fractions correctly.

> **Example**
> 32.47 should be read as thirty-two point four seven and not as thirty-two point forty-seven!

- When setting questions to test this topic, be very careful of the Instructional Objectives (I.O.) of the question.

> **Example**
> $$43.687 = 40 + 3 + \frac{6}{10} + \frac{8}{(\quad)} + \frac{7}{(\quad)}$$
>
> Avoid
>
> $$43.687 = 40 + 3 + \frac{3}{(\quad)} + \frac{2}{(\quad)} + \frac{7}{1000}$$
>
> (This tests more than just the concept of place values.)

1.3 Approximation and estimation

- For teaching the concepts of approximation and estimation, use the normal way of teaching rounding off. Get pupils to think if the decimal part is:
    - exactly half,
    - more than half, or
    - less than half.

- When rounding off to the nearest whole number, pupils tend to forget some digits if the whole number happens to be more than a digit. This useful tip may be of help:

> ***Example***
>
> Round off 16.67 to the nearest whole number.
>
> a) Ask pupils to circle the whole numbers with a pencil.
>
> (1 6). 6 7
>
> b) Underline the next number after the wanted whole number.
>
> (1 6) .6 7 — think whether the underlined number is 5 or greater.
>
> In this case, if the underlined number is 5 or greater, then the '16' increases only by 1, becoming '17'.
>
> c) Look at the circled numbers. The answer is therefore 17.

- For rounding off to 1 decimal place, do the same as above (circle both the whole numbers and the digit in the tenths place).

1.4 The decimal line

- The decimal line is important as it helps pupils to read scales.
- Quite often, pupils are unable to tell the value of a particular point given on a decimal line. More emphasis must be placed on how to arrive at the answers.
- You may want to start with the half-way mark between wholes etc. before proceeding to the finer division lines along the decimal line.

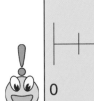

Example

'A' is half-way between '0' and '1'. The value of 'A' will be about 0.5 and for 'B', the value would be half-way between 2 and 3, hence 'B' is 2.5.

Example

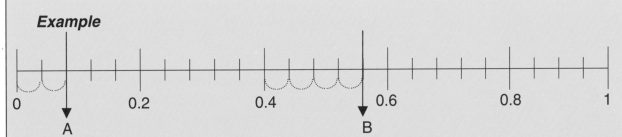

Here, you can teach pupils the skill of finding the value of one mark
($\approx$ one scallop).

$0.2 \div 5 = 0.04$
$0.04 \times 2 = 0.08$ (2 scallops from '0') — 'A'

$0.04 \times 4 = 0.16$ (4 scallops from '0.4')
$0.4 + 0.16 = 0.56$ — 'B'

1.5 Comparing/ordering decimals

- When teaching the comparison of decimal values, it would help pupils a great deal to line the decimals vertically such that the decimal points are in a line.

> **Example**
>
> Arrange from the smallest to the greatest: 9.34, 9.306, 9.342, 9.43
>
> Line them vertically (with the <u>decimal point</u> aligned) as shown:
>
> $$\downarrow$$
>
> 9.34
> 9.306
> 9.342
> 9.43
>
> Start comparing the whole numbers (from left to right).
> Continue with comparing the other decimal fractions (left to right).

1.6 Operations involving decimals

- Include division of decimals by a 1-digit whole number.
  (Division by 2-digit whole numbers will be taught in secondary school).
- Include multiplication of decimals by a whole number of up to 2 digits.
- Include multiplication and division of decimals by tens, hundreds and thousands.

> **Example**
>
> 9.76 × 34;   9.76 × 10;   9.76 × 200;   9.76 × 3 000
>
> 9.76 ÷ 5;   9.76 ÷ 10;   9.76 ÷ 200;   9.76 ÷ 3 000

- <u>Exclude</u> multiplication of decimals by decimals.

> **Example**
>
> 9.76 × 1.2

MENSURATION

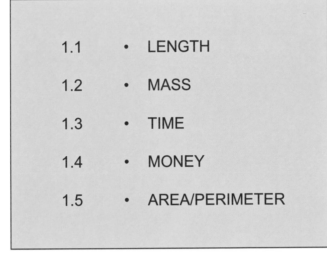

1.1	•	LENGTH
1.2	•	MASS
1.3	•	TIME
1.4	•	MONEY
1.5	•	AREA/PERIMETER

1.1 LENGTH

1.1.1 Measuring with non-standard units

- Many pupils encounter difficulties when the starting point is not at the beginning of a measuring instrument.
- Include exercises where the objects are placed at the starting point of a scale as well as after the starting point of the scale.
- It is good practice to indicate the relationship between the measuring instrument and the object to be measured. Dotted lines are used in this case.
- The objects must be labelled.

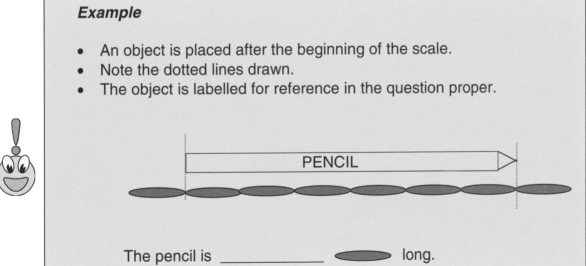

Example

- An object is placed after the beginning of the scale.
- Note the dotted lines drawn.
- The object is labelled for reference in the question proper.

PENCIL

The pencil is _____ ⬭ long.

1.1.2 Measuring in standard units

- Give pupils some hands-on activities in measuring lengths which do not start from the '0' mark.
- Encourage pupils to draw 'scallops' and count the number of scallops between the two ends of the picture.

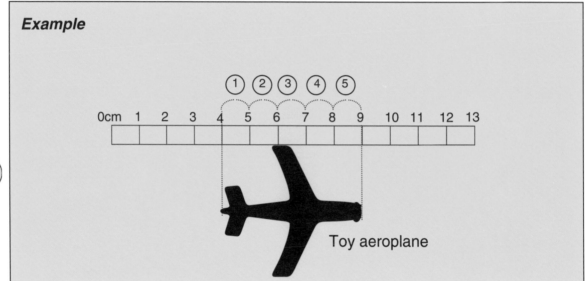

Example

Toy aeroplane

The toy aeroplane is _____ cm long.

1.1.3 Concept of m and cm

- Pupils may not be aware of the magnitude of m and cm. Mention some everyday objects and have pupils tell you if the unit should be m or cm.

Example

The tree is 2 _____ (m/cm) tall.

The boy is 142 _____ (m/cm) tall.

The whiteboard is 3 _____ (m/cm) long.

- This will create an awareness in pupils of the difference in length between metres (m) and centimetres (cm).

1.1.4 Comparison of lengths of objects

- Start with showing objects and getting pupils to estimate the lengths in cm.
- On the OHT, using a translucent/transparent ruler, get pupils to measure given objects starting from '0' cm. Proceed with measurements away from the '0' mark.
- Pupils have difficulty measuring objects which do not start from the mark '0'. The use of 'scallops' has proven to be a useful strategy.

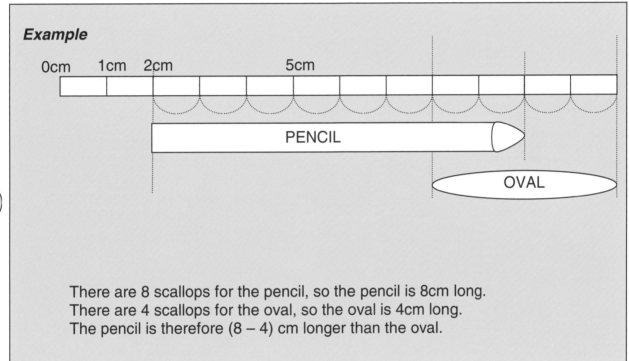

Example

There are 8 scallops for the pencil, so the pencil is 8cm long.
There are 4 scallops for the oval, so the oval is 4cm long.
The pencil is therefore (8 – 4) cm longer than the oval.

1.1.5 Estimation and measurement of length

- Our pupils are often unable to gauge lengths in everyday matters. Provide activities for pupils to estimate and measure lengths.
- The trundle wheel is a great machine for measuring distances. Let pupils make use of the trundle wheel. They may at the same time take note of their own walking pace.

A trundle wheel gives a clicking sound after a certain length is covered. Find out what that length is!

1.2 MASS

1.2.1 Reading the scale

- We have to bear in mind that our pupils are more exposed to digital displays of mass (or weight).
- Pupils have difficulty reading the kitchen scale when the markings are in-between calibrated labellings. You may want to help them look at the calibrations and teach them to find representations of the in-between values first.

1.2.2 Estimation and measurement of mass

- This is a very important skill as pupils are faced with such situations in their daily lives.

- Our pupils are very weak in estimating the mass of objects. Lots of hands-on activities will help them develop a sense of measurement. Perhaps the following sequence would be of help to them.

a) Compare several objects by 'weighing' with the hands and list them from heaviest to lightest. Objects could include big but light ones. Pupils could compare the weight of their own belongings too. Then have them fill up systematically on a pre-prepared worksheet. (Refer to **Annex MSN-1**.)

b) Give each pupil a pre-weighed piece of plasticine** and tell them the mass. (They should know how to weigh objects at this level). Using the plasticine, they then proceed to estimate the mass of the objects in (a) and fill up the results in a worksheet. (Refer to **Annex MSN-1**.)

c) Provide pupils with opportunities to measure the objects with standard weighing scales and record the actual measurements. In this way, they will be able to see how accurate their estimations are when compared to the actual measurements. They can then record the actual weights of the objects in their worksheets. If their estimation skill shows a need for reinforcement, the teacher may want to redo Steps (b) and (c) to help them to improve their skill.

> ** As pupils weigh objects, they learn to estimate the mass by comparing them against established references (in this case, the plasticine). Mental models for masses allow pupils to estimate the mass of unfamiliar objects.

1.3 TIME

1.3.1 Recognising the 'hands'

- Concentrate on the words 'half past'. Help pupils to see the difference between the length of the minute hand and that of the hour hand. Explain also the presence of the second hand in most analog clocks and watches.

1.3.2 Telling/writing time

- Bring to pupils' attention the fact that in 'half past', the hour hand is always found between two numbers.
- Recapitulate the o'clock, half-past, quarter-past, etc. Do lots of oral work.
- Make abundant use of 'analog' clocks for pupils, one for each pupil.
- Recapitulate the 5 times table.
- Then go on to minutes past.

Example
Draw 2 hands on the clock face to show half-past two.

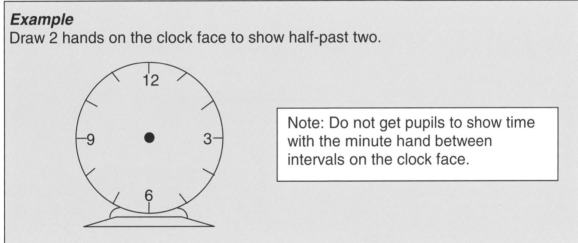

Note: Do not get pupils to show time with the minute hand between intervals on the clock face.

1.3.3 Time duration

- A time line can be used to illustrate the time frame.

Example
May travelled from 9.30 a.m. to 2.50 p.m. How long did she travel?

- Use hourly 'scallops'

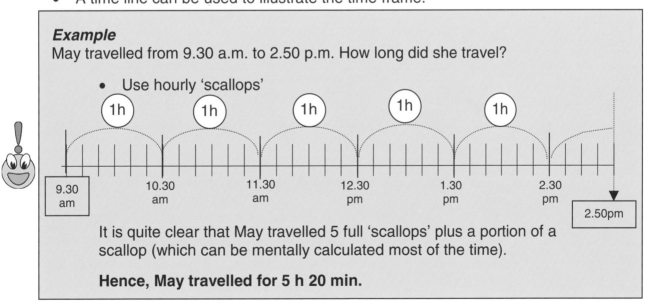

It is quite clear that May travelled 5 full 'scallops' plus a portion of a scallop (which can be mentally calculated most of the time).

Hence, May travelled for 5 h 20 min.

- Provide exercises to show the relationship between hours and minutes.

- Remind pupils to be very cautious when calculating time taken and the time itself.

> **Example**
>
> Jim started doing his homework at 8.25 a.m. and took 2 h 55 min to complete it. At what time did he stop work?
>
> 8.25 + 2.55 = 11.20 ⎫
> He stopped at 11.20 a.m. ⎬ This is a very common mistake!
> ⎭

- Actual time (8.25 a.m.) and duration of time (2 h 55 min) cannot be added!

- Use 'count on' method:

> **Example**
>
> Jim started doing his homework at 8.25 a.m. and took 2 h 55 min to complete it. At what time did he stop work?
>
> 8.25 a.m. $\xrightarrow{\ +\,2\,h\ }$ 10.25 a.m. $\xrightarrow{\ +\,55\,min\ }$ 11.20 a.m.
>
> Using this method, no mathematical statement is needed as pupils can do this mentally !
>
> If pupils are unable to calculate mentally, get them to use the time line with 'scallops'.
>
>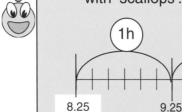
>
> **2 h 55 min from 8.25 a.m. will be 11.20 a.m.**

Time ... cont'd

- Take special note of the addition and subtraction of compound units, especially those found in years and months, as in the average age of people.

Example

The table shows the ages of 3 children as of January 2000.

Name	Age
Amy	9 years 8 months
Baozhu	10 years 7 months
Cailing	11 years 6 months

a) What is their total age?
b) What is their average age?
   (*Pupils will have to remember not to add in terms of base-ten.*)

- Since the 24-h clock has become part and parcel of everyday life, it would be beneficial if we could also include the 24-h clock in our enrichment activities. This will help bridge school mathematics with real-life mathematics.

- It erases confusion over the a.m. and p.m. status as used in the 12-h clock.

- The military uses it to avoid misunderstandings of meeting times.

- The digital clock and watch are used widely, exhibiting the 24-h clock function.

Therefore

9 o'clock in the morning…	Half past two in the afternoon…
0900h is the same as, or	1430h is the same as, or
09:00 (*as shown on most digital clocks/watches*)	14:30(*as shown on most digital clocks/watches*)

1.4 MONEY

1.4.1 Addition/subtraction of money

- Have group activities to simulate buying and selling using 'play' money.
- Start with coin combinations (eg. two 5¢ coins = one 10¢ coin etc...)

> **Note:**
> At Primary One, many pupils are not very articulate with the value of money taking the form of different coin combinations!

- When teaching addition and subtraction of 'Money' to Primary One pupils, separate the dollars and cents.

> **Example**
> 20 cents + 60 cents = 80 cents
> 20¢ + 60¢ = 80¢
> $2 + $8 = $10

- Exclude sums like '$2 + 60¢' as they are not in the Primary One syllabus.

- In the syllabus for 2001, addition and subtraction of money in compound units (not in decimal notation) are taught at Primary Two while addition and subtraction of money in compound units (using decimal notation) are taught at Primary Three.

- The rationale behind avoiding decimal notation when teaching 'Money' in Primary Two is that we want to teach pupils to add or subtract without formal algorithm. We can use the 'make a dollar' or 'break a dollar' method to help pupils consolidate the concept of money. However, this stage is often skipped and pupils go straight onto adding money in decimal notation as in adding decimals.

- At Primary Two, the addition and subtraction of 'Money' include only compound units and not in decimal notation yet.

> **Example**
> $4.20 + 75¢ = $4.95
> $4 + $2 = $6
> 60¢ + $2.20 = $2.80
> $5.00 − 80¢ = $4.20

- Exclude $4.20 + $0.75.

- It would be authentic if specimen copies of real money could be used for the teaching and learning of 'Money'. However, be aware of the consequences of photocopying real money!

1.4.2 Written representation of money in decimal notation

- Teach pupils to write money in words.

> **Example**
>
> $7.25 — seven dollars and twenty-five cents
>
> $8 345.39 — eight thousand, three hundred and forty-five dollars and thirty-nine cents

- For computation, help pupils to be more aware of the need to align the decimal points in formal algorithm.

> **Example**
>
> $$\begin{array}{r} \$6.38 \\ + \ \$7.99 \\ \hline . \\ \hline \end{array}$$

- Point out to pupils the right and wrong ways of writing money.

Example

Fourteen dollars and ninety cents

$14.90	Correct	
1490¢	Correct	Help pupils to get used to showing answers in the simplest form ($14.90)
$14.9	Incorrect	Explain that decimal notation of cents should be in two places.
$14.09¢	Incorrect	Note that the two units ($, ¢) should not appear at the same time in decimal notation.
$1409¢	Incorrect	Note that the two units ($, ¢) should not appear at the same time.

1.5 AREA & PERIMETER

1.5.1 Area in non-standard/standard units

- Start with getting pupils to colour areas of given figures.
- Have pupils see the difference between areas and perimeters by asking them to show perimeters of given figures in specified colours.

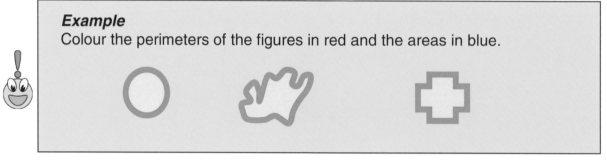

Example
Colour the perimeters of the figures in red and the areas in blue.

- Include perimeters of irregular figures with 'hidden' dimensions.

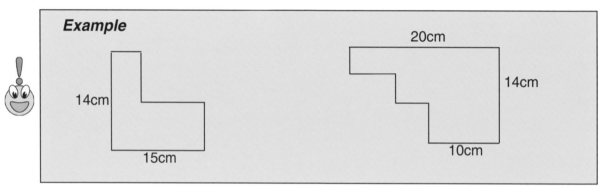

Example

14cm
15cm

20cm
14cm
10cm

- <u>Avoid</u> asking ambiguous questions like:

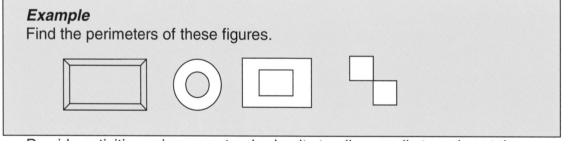

Example
Find the perimeters of these figures.

- Provide activities using non-standard units to allow pupils to arrive at the conclusion that using non-standard units is not very accurate for comparisons. This will help them understand the need to use standard units (for example, cm^2).

Example
Measure the length of a whiteboard using handspans.
(Pupils will notice that the answers are greatly varied. This will show them the need for standardisation.)

- Encourage pupils to read aloud 'cm^2' as square centimetres and not cm two or cm squared or centimetre squared, etc.

Example

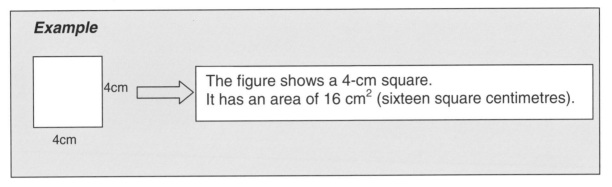

4cm

4cm

The figure shows a 4-cm square.
It has an area of 16 cm^2 (sixteen square centimetres).

1.5.2 Area of figures made up of squares

- Provide hands-on activities. Pupils can make use of 'square-shaped' papers and come up with different figures of the same area. Put their 'masterpieces' up on the class bulleting board.

Example

On the given 1-cm grid, show different figures with an area of 6cm^2.

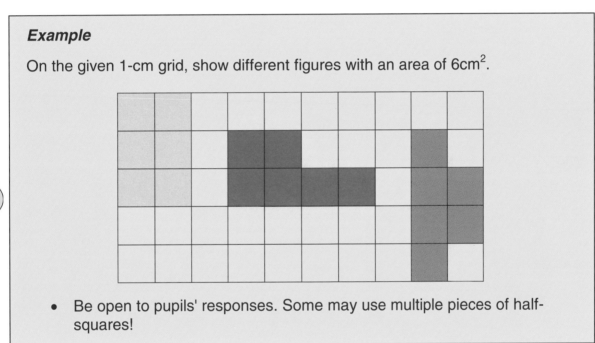

- Be open to pupils' responses. Some may use multiple pieces of half-squares!

- After the pupils have grasped the concept of area of squares, help them to see the 'square' numbers in solving related figures.

Example

The figure below, not drawn to scale, is made up of 2 squares.
The total area of the figure is 45cm^2. Its length is a whole number.
What is the length of one side of the smaller square?

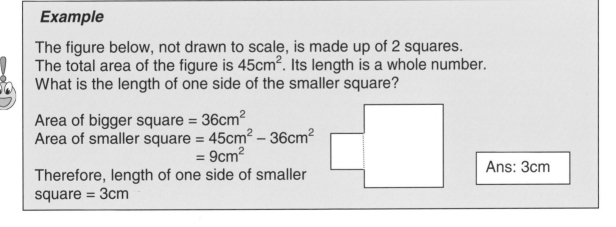

Area of bigger square = 36cm^2
Area of smaller square = 45cm^2 – 36cm^2
$\qquad\qquad\qquad$ = 9cm^2
Therefore, length of one side of smaller square = 3cm

Ans: 3cm

1.5.3 Area of triangles

- Help pupils to visualise the fact that the area of a triangle is always half the area of its related rectangle.

Example 1

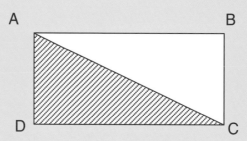

The related rectangle is Rectangle ABCD. (Emphasise same height and base.)

Therefore, area of Triangle ADC is $\frac{1}{2}$ area of Rectangle ABCD.

Example 2

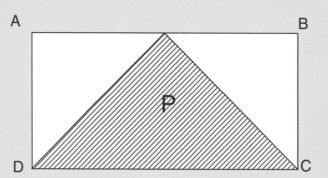

Area of Triangle P = $\frac{1}{2}$ area of Rectangle ABCD

(Related rectangle has same height and base as Triangle P.)

- For obtuse triangles, pupils may need hands-on activities.
  (Refer to **Annex MSN-2** for exercises for pupils to comprehend the concept of related rectangles.)

Example

Area of Triangle BDF = $\frac{1}{2}$ Area of Rectangle ADFE.

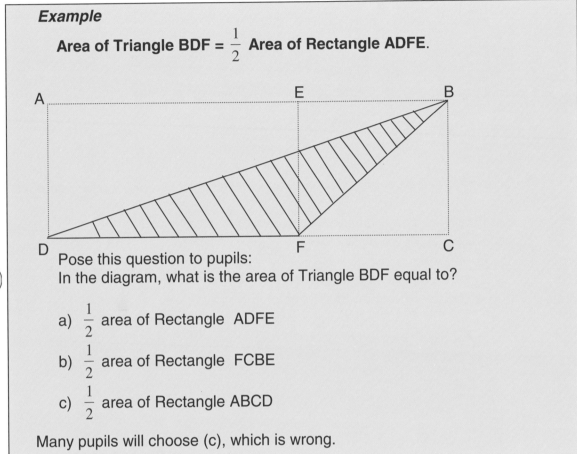

Pose this question to pupils:
In the diagram, what is the area of Triangle BDF equal to?

a) $\frac{1}{2}$ area of Rectangle ADFE

b) $\frac{1}{2}$ area of Rectangle FCBE

c) $\frac{1}{2}$ area of Rectangle ABCD

Many pupils will choose (c), which is wrong.

- Pupils find it difficult to identify the correct height (altitude) with the correct base of the triangle. Provide ample practice in matching the correct heights with the corresponding bases in triangles.

Example (*Use the 'chair-sitting' clue*)

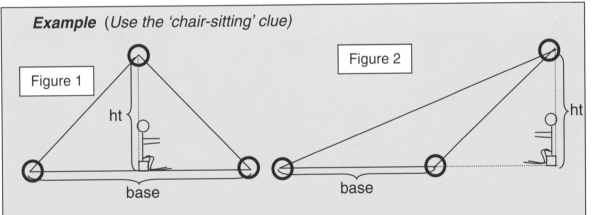

Note: If the height is within the triangle (Fig.1), then the feet are always on the base which is the distance between 2 vertices of the said triangle. Otherwise, the feet are on the extension of the base where the height is outside the triangle (Fig.2). Then the back is always against the height which is the distance between the base (or its extension) and the remaining vertex.

1.5.4 Area and perimeter of circles

Drawing circles

- Ensure that pupils have their compasses with them. Teach them how to draw circles with the compass. They are not very adept in using the compass for this purpose.
- Ensure that pencils are sharp.
- Pupils should not rotate the paper/exercise books. They should rotate only the compass.
- Merge art and craft lessons with the drawing of circles. Make patterns! Let pupils try drawing circles with the compass.

Relationship between the circumference and diameter of a circle

- Get pupils to draw 2 circles of different radii (3cm and 4cm) on a prepared worksheet (refer to **Annex MSN-3**) and fill in the necessary data as shown in the worksheet.
- Put a cut along the circumference as a starting point.
- Use a string to measure the distance round each circle. Record data.

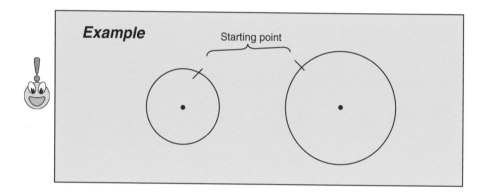

Introducing π (pi)

- Let pupils compare the circumference of each circle with its diameter.
- It would be more convincing to try out with even more circles and then record their circumferences against the diameters. Pupils will discover that the circumference is ≈ 3 times the diameter of the circle.
- The approximate constant is interpreted as π (≈ 3.142 or $\frac{22}{7}$).

1.5.5. Area of circles versus area of rectangles

- By now pupils are very familiar with areas of rectangles. So tap on their knowledge to enhance their understanding of area of circles.
- Provide hands-on activities for them to visualise how π helps in getting the area of a circle.
- Once they 'see' how the area of a circle is derived, they can go ahead and memorise the formula for finding the area of a circle.

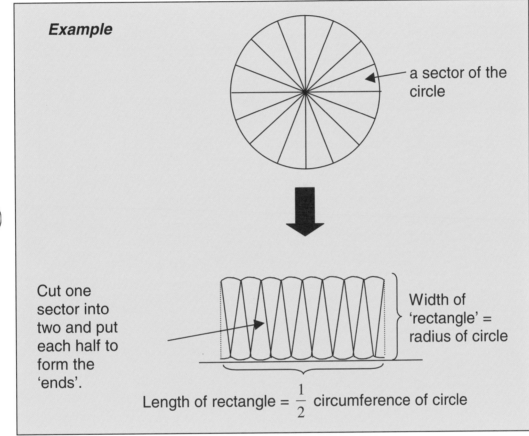

Example

a sector of the circle

Cut one sector into two and put each half to form the 'ends'.

Width of 'rectangle' = radius of circle

Length of rectangle = $\frac{1}{2}$ circumference of circle

- (Refer to **Annex MSN-4** for the actual worksheet.)

STATISTICS

1. Graphs

- Include activities that provide opportunities for pupils to

  — explore statistics in real-life situations systematically.
  — systematically collect, organise and describe data.
  — construct, read and interpret tables, charts and graphs.
  — make inferences and evaluate arguments that are based on data analysis.
  — develop an appreciation for statistical methods as powerful means for decision making.

1.1 Bar graphs/column graphs

One to one representation

- Start with charts (eg. birthdays). Give pupils a sticker each and get them to stick the sticker on the column of his birthday month. Discuss the representation.
- Continue with 'scales' (eg. one to five representation)
- Ask questions regarding the representations.

Example 1

If 1 circle represents 5 toys, what do 2 circles, 3 circles, 4 circles etc. represent?

Continue with the other way round:

Example 2

If I have 5 toys, I will draw 1 circle on the chart. What if I have 10 toys, 15 toys, etc?

- Make it a practice among pupils to write the actual value of the bar/column representation near the bar/column. This will help them to answer questions that follow.

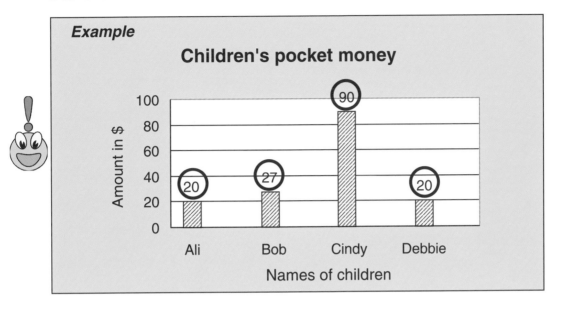

1.2 Line graphs

- Pupils need to be taught how to read the data in line graphs. Sometimes, we assume that since pupils perform well in bar/column graphs, it is all right to go straight into the exercises pertaining to line graphs. However, studies have shown that pupils do get confused with line graphs, especially with the vertical and horizontal axes looking almost the same.
- Help pupils read as well as interpret the data shown on the line graph.
- Pupils find difficulty in seeing the relationship between the vertical and horizontal axes. Give them oral exercises to talk about the graph and let them ask questions.
- Get pupils to draw 'dotted' lines to join the connection between data from the vertical to the horizontal axes.

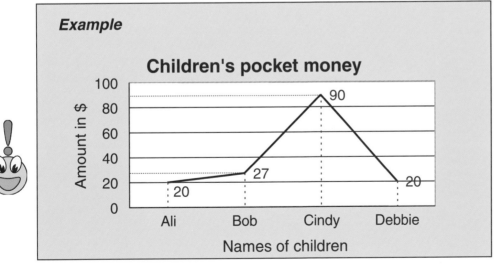

1.3 Pie charts

- Solving problems using information given in a pie chart will be covered in the secondary syllabus. In the Primary Mathematics syllabus, all questions on the pie chart should be directly related to the information given in the chart.
- In statistical representation, ask questions whose answers can be obtained from the graph itself without many steps.

Example 1

Mary spent her pocket money on stationery. The pie chart shows how her money was spent.

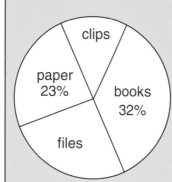

Include:
a) What did Mary spend most of her money on?
b) What percentage of her money was spent on files?
c) What percentage of her money was spent on clips?
d) If Mary spent $5.40 on clips, how much did she spend altogether?

Include (d), which is dependent on (c), only if (c) is asked explicitly.

Example 2

The pie chart shows the number of pupils interested in the respective CCAs.

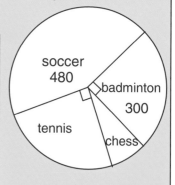

Include:
a) What fraction of the total number of pupils was interested in tennis?
b) How many pupils were there in the school?
c) How many pupils were interested in chess?
d) What % of the total number of pupils were interested in soccer?
e) What was the ratio of the number of pupils who were interested in badminton to those interested in chess?

The information in (b) should be worked out before (c), (d) and (e) are asked.

GEOMETRY

1.1 ANGLES

- An angle is a figure formed by two rays (sides of the angle) that extend from a common point (the vertex of the angle).

1.1.1 Identifying right angles

- Help pupils to identify the right angles when asked for the number of right angles in a given figure.

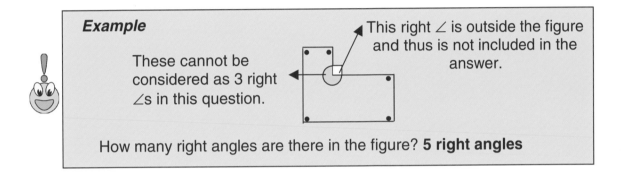

Example

These cannot be considered as 3 right ∠s in this question.

This right ∠ is outside the figure and thus is not included in the answer.

How many right angles are there in the figure? **5 right angles**

1.1.2 Angles formed by parallel lines

- Corresponding and alternate angles which are associated with parallel lines are not in the Primary Mathematics syllabus.

1.1.3 Measuring angles

- Relate acute angles (less than 90°) to right angles which was learnt in Primary 3. Pupils can then estimate angles using the right angle (90°) as reference.

- For measurement purposes, use a normal transparent protractor and then make enlarged copies on the OHT for projection on the OHP. This will help pupils identify better with their own protractors.

- Highlight to pupils the reason for having the two layers of markings on the protractor. This is to ease measurement depending on which direction the angle to be measured is facing.

- Show pupils how to measure 2 similar angles facing different directions. They must know that an angle is always encompassed by two arms so one of the arms must face the '0' mark and the readings would then come from that row of markings.

Using the protractor

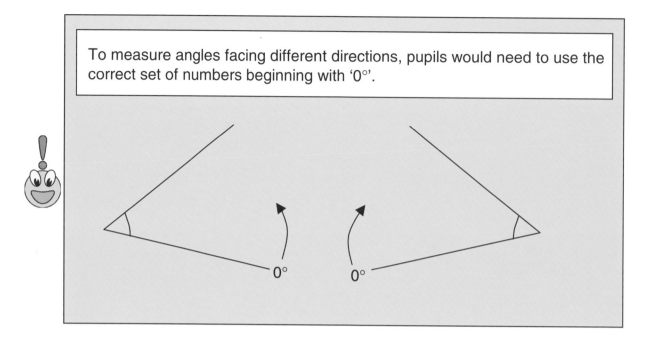

To measure angles facing different directions, pupils would need to use the correct set of numbers beginning with '0°'.

0°   0°

- Pupils have difficulty in measuring reflex angles. Teach them to 'divide' the angle into two parts, one of which is the 180° before measuring the 'other' angle. Then add the two up. Alternatively, minus the 'other' angle from 360°.

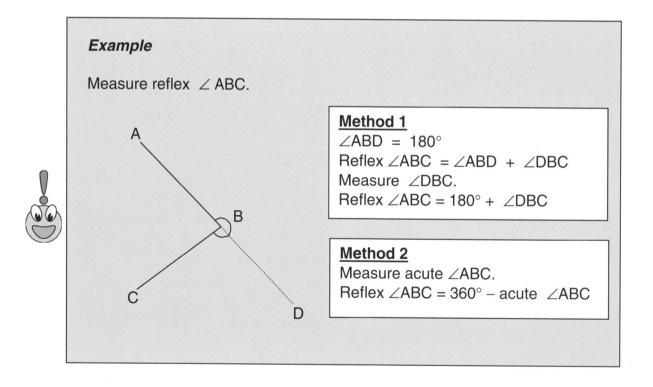

Example

Measure reflex ∠ABC.

A

B

C

D

Method 1
∠ABD = 180°
Reflex ∠ABC = ∠ABD + ∠DBC
Measure ∠DBC.
Reflex ∠ABC = 180° + ∠DBC

Method 2
Measure acute ∠ABC.
Reflex ∠ABC = 360° − acute ∠ABC

1.2 SYMMETRY (LINE)

- Introduce symmetry through art:

  — Have pupils apply wet paint on one side of a sheet of paper.
  — Before the paint dries, fold the paper. An identical (but mirror-image) pattern would be seen.

- Talk to pupils about symmetry in the classroom, extending it to the environment, etc.
- The line of symmetry on a symmetric figure divides the figure into two parts which fit exactly.

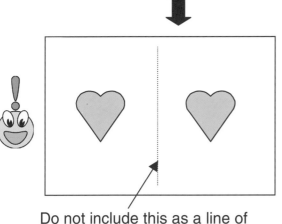 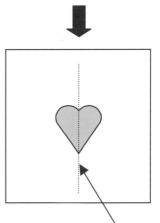

Do not include this as a line of symmetry of the figure (the heart shape) as it is not on the figure.

This is a line of symmetry.

- Pupils have difficulty in drawing the other half of the given shape where the line of symmetry is neither horizontal nor vertical.

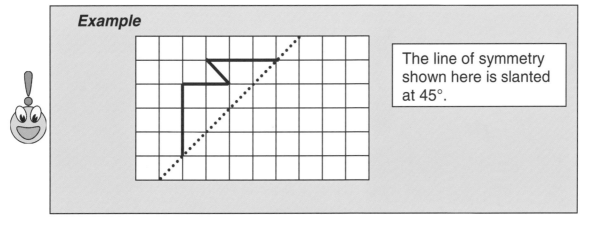

Example

The line of symmetry shown here is slanted at 45°.

- Discuss the importance of symmetry in our lives.
  (The computer courseware 'Mirror Symmetry' is useful in bringing real-life symmetry into the classroom.)

- **Exclude rotational symmetry**

  — This is an example of rotational symmetry. It is for your information only; it is not included in the Primary Mathematics syllabus.

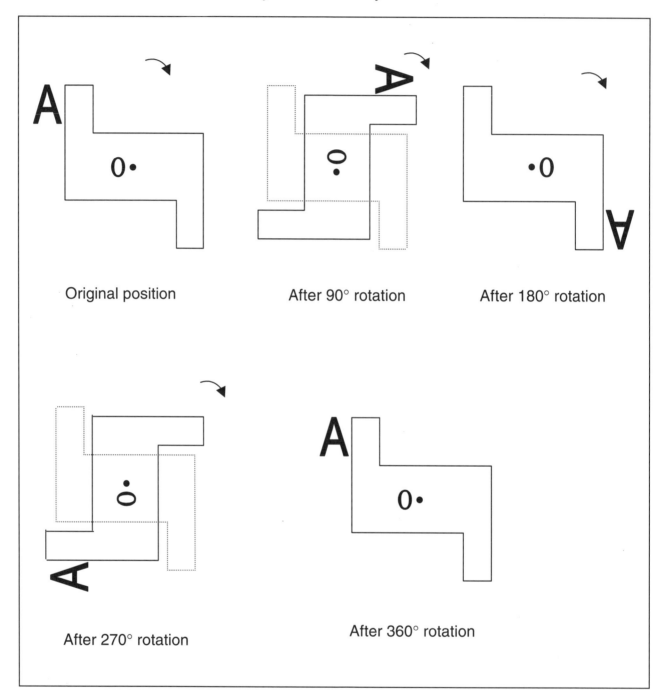

Original position

After 90° rotation

After 180° rotation

After 270° rotation

After 360° rotation

  — Since the cut-out figure coincides with the original figure twice within a 360° rotation about the point O, we say that this figure has rotational symmetry about O and its order of rotational symmetry is 2.

1.3 Tessellation

- Tessellation is a tiled pattern formed by repeating figures to fill a plane without gaps or overlaps.
- A tessellation extends infinitely in all directions.

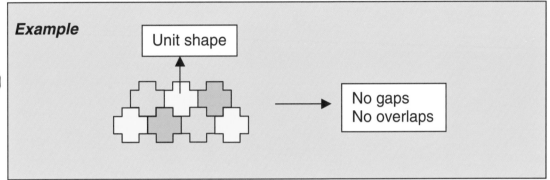

- Explain what tessellation is about. Cite examples of ceramic tiles on the floor.
- Ask pupils to comment on the tile patterns that can be found in school, especially on the walls and the floor.
- Discuss unit shapes that can tessellate.
  (Examples include squares, rectangles, different types of triangles, etc.)
- Make use of the PMP materials on Tessellation (Shapes) and get pupils to study the tessellating effects in groups.
- Present some shapes (as shown in **Annex GEO-1**) and get pupils to discuss in groups/pairs as to which shapes can tessellate.

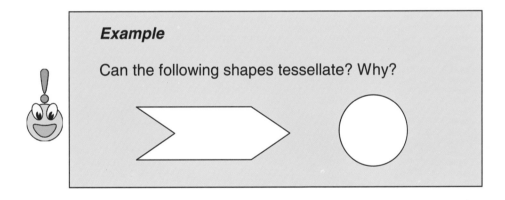

- Introduce the 'Microsoft Paint' programme to the pupils. This programme is found in all computers operating on the Microsoft platform.

TESSELLATION using Information Technology (IT)

- Go to **Start**.
- Go to **Programme**.
- Go to **Accessories**.
- Go to **Paint**.
- Follow the instructions shown below.

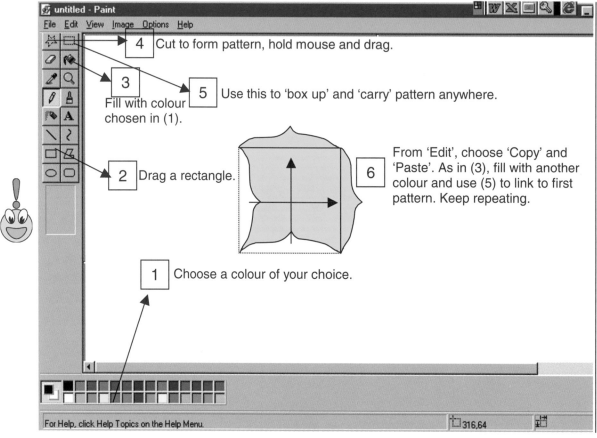

untitled - Paint

File Edit View Image Options Help

| 4 | Cut to form pattern, hold mouse and drag.

| 3 |
Fill with colour chosen in (1).

| 5 | Use this to 'box up' and 'carry' pattern anywhere.

| 2 | Drag a rectangle.

| 6 | From 'Edit', choose 'Copy' and 'Paste'. As in (3), fill with another colour and use (5) to link to first pattern. Keep repeating.

| 1 | Choose a colour of your choice.

For Help, click Help Topics on the Help Menu.   316,64

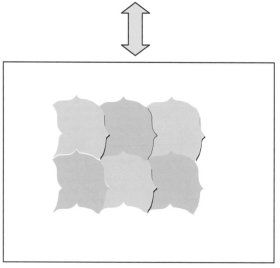

1.4 Nets

- Start with actual objects (eg. boxes). However, remove the extra flap used for 'tucking in' so that we are left with only 6 squares. With a cutter, open up the box at the edges in pupils' presence. Draw the arrangement on the board. Discuss. Introduce the word 'nets.'
- Use manipulatives (of durable plastic). In their groups, get pupils to make nets of cubes with six connectable squares. Show them how to make a cube and then open out to see the various nets. Have them draw their nets on the board. Get them to formulate 'rules' for determining the nets of cubes. (Pupils can try **Annex GEO-2**.)
- The following nets 'rules' were by pupils who were assigned the task of formulating 'rules' for determining the nets of cubes.

— When the longest panel has 4 squares, the remaining 2 are to be placed anywhere on either side, with one on each side.

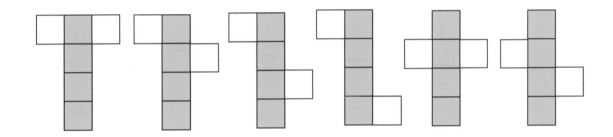

— When the longest panel has 3 squares, the remaining 3 are to be placed anywhere on either side such that there will always be at least 2 free edges on either side.

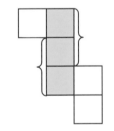 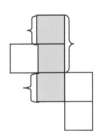 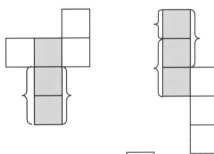

— When the longest panel has 2 squares, the remaining 4 are fairly distributed on either side such that there will always be only one free edge. This is the only possible nets of a cube with 2 squares as its longest 'panel.'

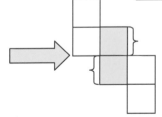

89

NETS OF CUBOIDS

- Start with comparisons of adjacent lines which are equal in length: Lines 1, then lines 2, 3 and 4. The remaining Lines 5 are equal. The final Lines 6, though opposite to each other, are equal. So this can be a net of a cuboid.

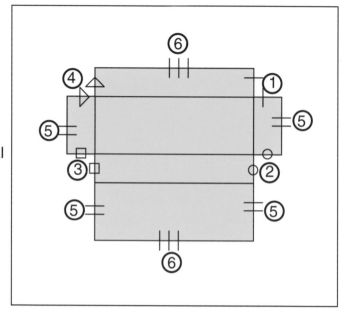

- Remember to start with adjacent lines and compare their lengths. Be systematic.
- For 'left-over' lines, look at their immediate adjacents for relationships.

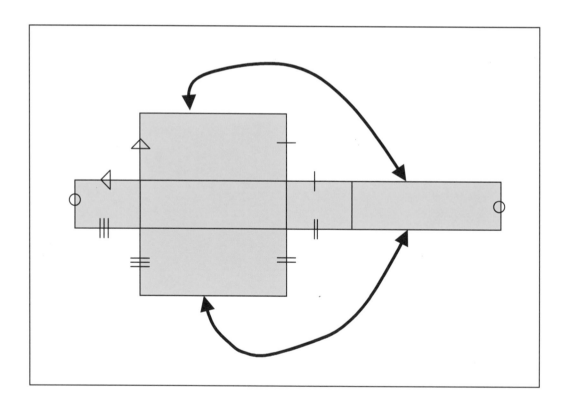

- Let pupils try **Annex GEO-3**.

PERCENTAGE

1.1 Percent

- Percent expresses a relationship between a number and 100.
- The % indicates a denominator of 100. It means 'per hundred' or 'out of 100'.
- For example, 26% is an expression of the ratio between the numbers 26 and 100. It means 26 parts of 100, or 26 out of 100.

1.2 Relating percentage to the real world

- Show pupils newspaper cut-outs of sales items where % is prominently displayed.
- Discuss the advantages of using % instead of fixed sums, eg. instead of a straight $10 discount, a 10% discount is given.
- Because of the use of % in real life situations, it is important to equip pupils with the ability to estimate percent of quantities.

1.3 Connecting percent with decimals and fractions

- Percent is simply hundredths. Percent then can be substituted for the expression of common fractions and simple decimals as hundredths.

> **Example**
>
> Consider $\dfrac{3}{4}$.
>
> As a fraction expressed in hundredths, it is $\dfrac{75}{100}$.
>
> This is the same as 75% (i.e. 75 out of a hundred).

- Percent is not a new concept, only a new notation and terminology. Connections with fractions and decimal concepts are developmentally appropriate.

1.4 The Base

- When dealing with percentage, the base '100' must always be taken into consideration. Help pupils to identify the base. Give ample practice on identification of bases before embarking on the problem-solving.
(Refer to **Annex PER-1** for more exercises.)

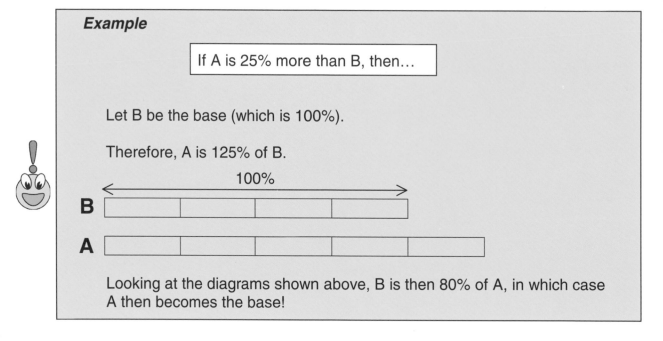

Example

If A is 25% more than B, then...

Let B be the base (which is 100%).

Therefore, A is 125% of B.

Looking at the diagrams shown above, B is then 80% of A, in which case A then becomes the base!

- Make use of conversion to fractions.

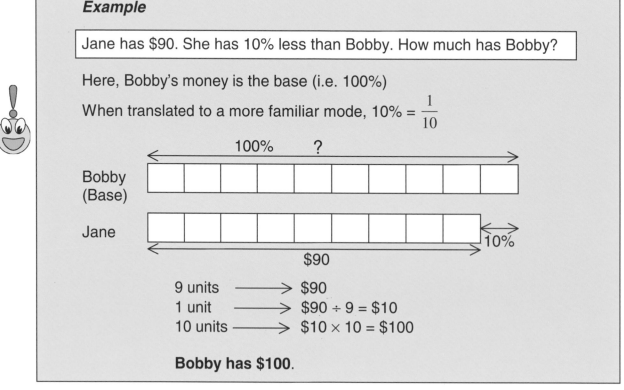

Example

Jane has $90. She has 10% less than Bobby. How much has Bobby?

Here, Bobby's money is the base (i.e. 100%)

When translated to a more familiar mode, $10\% = \dfrac{1}{10}$

9 units ⟶ $90
1 unit ⟶ $90 ÷ 9 = $10
10 units ⟶ $10 × 10 = $100

Bobby has $100.

- A point of confusion arises when a given rate is applied to different bases.

Example

Consider the result when the price of a $50 book is increased by 20%.
(This raises the price to $60.) Later, the price is reduced to $50.
Is the rate (percent) of decrease the same as the rate of increase?
Both times, the amount involved is $10 (up or down).

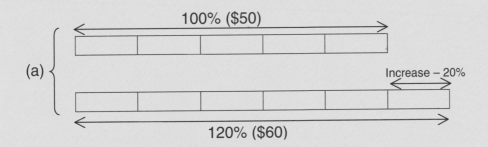

(a)

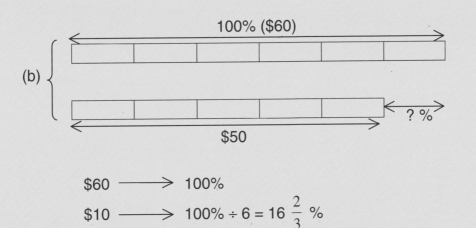

(b)

$60 ⟶ 100%

$10 ⟶ 100% ÷ 6 = $16\frac{2}{3}$ %

The decrease in (b) is $16\frac{2}{3}$ % and not 20% as in (a), although for both times, the amount involved is $10.

1.5 Use of percentage and the 'equal sign'

- Remind pupils of the proper way to represent values in percentage.

Example

$$\frac{2}{5} \times 100\% = 40\% \qquad \frac{2}{5} \times 100 = 40\%$$

Enrichment Activities

Enrichment activities are a valuable part of a mathematics programme. They provide opportunities for pupils to:

- develop, reinforce, enhance and extend mathematical concepts and skills,
- stimulate and develop thinking skills and problem-solving strategies,
- develop a sense of enquiry,
- engage in imaginative and creative work arising from mathematical ideas, and
- work cooperatively and explore all possibilities in various mathematical situations.

Types of enrichment activities:

- Investigative work
- Problem-solving
- Project work
- Mathematics trail
- Games, puzzles and quizzes, etc.

Enrichment activities should be challenging tasks that involve pupils in some of the following processes:

- Gathering data
- Observing outcomes
- Looking for references
- Identifying and determining patterns and relationships
- Measuring lengths, masses and time
- Analysing situations
- Graphing information and results
- Communicating findings in written reports or oral presentations

Designing the activities:

Ask these questions:
- What is the specific objective of the activity?
- What is the essential conceptual content in the activity?
- What problem-solving processes might be observed?
- What thinking skills might be demonstrated?
- What opportunities might be provided to observe communication skills?
- Are there possibilities for pupils to connect the content with other content either within or outside mathematics?
- How can the activity be extended?
- Is the activity accessible to a range of pupils?
- How would you begin an after-activity discussion?

Throw the rings!

A practice activity for addition of three numbers

In the figure, the score with the three rings is 10.
That is, 2 + 3 + 5 = 10.

Two or three rings could also go on the same number.
Hence, you may also score 10 with the rings at 2, 2 and 6.

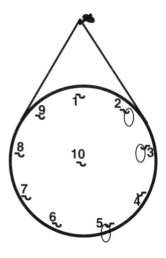

1. Find some other ways of scoring 10 with 3 rings.
   List as many different ways as you can. (Note: 3 + 2 + 5,
   2 + 3 + 5, 3 + 5 + 2, 3 + 5 + 2, 5 + 3 + 2 and 5 + 2 + 3 are
   counted as the same way.)

2. Find as many ways as you can of scoring 15 with 3 rings.

3. What is the highest possible score with three rings? All three rings must score.

4. What is the lowest possible score with three rings? All three rings must score.

5. If all three rings landed on the same hook, what are all the possible scores?

6. 4 rings landed on some hooks to give a score of 20. 3 of the rings landed on the
   same hook. Where did the 4th ring land?

Refer to Page 121 for the answers

Triangular numbers & square numbers

- The numbers 1, 3 and 6 are called *triangular numbers*.
- The numbers 1, 4 and 9 are called *square numbers*.
- These numbers can be represented by dots in certain geometrical configurations, and they are a link between geometry and arithmetic.

Triangular Numbers T_n

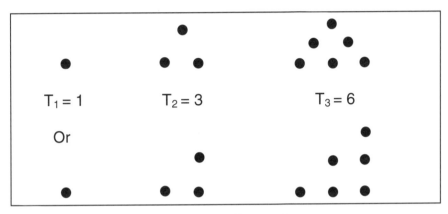

$T_1 = 1$ $T_2 = 3$ $T_3 = 6$

Or

Square Numbers S_n

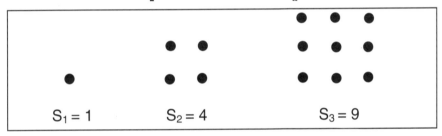

$S_1 = 1$ $S_2 = 4$ $S_3 = 9$

1. Look at the dot patterns above and list the next 3 triangular numbers and square numbers in the table below. Complete the table.

Position n^{th}	Triangular numbers T_n	Sum	Square numbers S_n	Product/sum of square numbers
1st	1	$1 = 1$	1	$1 = 1 \times 1 = 1$
2nd	3	$3 = 1 + 2$	4	$4 = 2 \times 2 = 1 + 3$
3rd	6	$6 = 1 + 2 + 3$	9	$9 = 3 \times 3 = 3 + 6$
4th				
5th				
6th				

2. With the help of the number pattern in the table, write down the 10th triangular number and the 10th square number.

3. Name a rule for T_n and for S_n in terms of n.

4. Write down and explain a relation between T_n and S_n.

Refer to Page 121 for the answers

Arranging chairs

An activity on using arrays

Find as many ways as you can to arrange 12 chairs so that each row contains the same number of chairs.

Draw the arrangements in the grid below.

Arrangement of 12 chairs

	x	x	x	x	x	x	
	x	x	x	x	x	x	
		2	x	6			

1.   How many different arrangements can you form? List them.

2.   How would you arrange 6 chairs so that there are the same number of chairs in each row?

3.   How would you arrange 7 chairs so that there are the same number of chairs in each row?

Please turn over ...

98

4. Complete the table.

No. of chairs	No. of rows	No. of chairs in a row	Kind of no.*
6	1 2 3 6	6 3 2 1	
7			
8			
9			
10			
11			
12			
13			
14			
15			
16			
17			
18			
19			
20			

5. *When there are only two arrangements, the number is called a *prime number*. List all the prime numbers between 6 and 20.

6. *When there are more than two arrangements, the number is a *composite number*. For some composite numbers, it is possible to form an arrangement with the same number of chairs per row as there are rows. These numbers are called *square numbers*. List all the square numbers between 6 and 20.

Refer to Page 122 for the answers

Factors and multiples

- The *multiples* of any given number are obtained by multiplying the number in turn by each of the natural numbers 1, 2, 3, etc.

- A *factor* is one of two or more numbers that when multiplied together yield a given product.

Spotting multiples

- Every natural number is a multiple of 1.
- Multiples of 2 are even numbers. The last digit of the multiples is either 0, 2, 4, 6 or 8.
- The digital sum of a multiple of 3 is always a multiple of 3; the digital root is always 3, 6 or 9.
- The last 2 digits of a multiple of 4 are themselves a multiple of 4.
- The multiples of 5 always end in 0 or 5.
- Multiples of 6 are multiples of 2 and multiples of 3; so they must be even and have a digital root of 3, 6, or 9.
- The last 3 digits of a multiple of 8 must be a multiple of 8.
- The digital sum of a multiple of 9 is always a multiple of 9; the digital root is always 9.
- The multiples of 10 always end in 0.
- For multiples of 11, the difference of the sum of digits in the odd places and the sum of the digits in the even places is either 0 or is a multiple of 11.
  Example,

$$2\ 0\ 9\ 3\ 3$$

$$2 + 9 + 3 = 14 \qquad 0 + 3 = 3$$

$$14 - 3 = 11$$

Hence, 20 933 is divisible by 11.

Teaching points

- Encourage pupils to be fascinated by numbers and patterns in numbers.
- Build up pupils' confidence in responding to numerical situations by exploring the concepts and properties of factors, multiples and prime numbers.
- Illustrate the transitive property of 'is a factor of' and 'is a multiple of'.

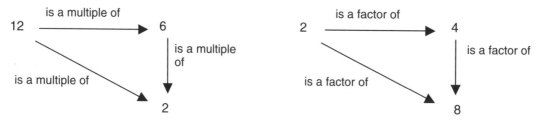

- Share with pupils some of the ways of testing various multiples.
- Use calculators to explore factors and multiples.
- Use rectangle arrays to illustrate the concepts of factors (prime numbers and composite numbers for enrichment).

How long would it take you to count to one billion?

Do you know that:
  - a million is 1 000 000;
  - a billion is 1 000 000 000; and
  - a trillion is 1 000 000 000 000?
Can you imagine how big these numbers are?

The following analogies may help you to understand their relative magnitudes better: A million hours ago was in the late 19th century, but a billion hours ago was over 100 000 years ago — a pre-historic time. If a marble of diameter 1.3cm were magnified so that its diameter were one million times as large, it would be a sphere with a diameter of about 13km. If the marble were magnified so that its diameter were one billion times as large, it would be a sphere of the size of the earth!

Activity

(You may use a calculator to do this activity.)

1. Assuming you could count one number every second,

   a) estimate the approximate time it would take to count from 1 to 1 million.

      (i) _____ seconds

      (ii) _____ minutes

      (iii) _____ hours

      (iv) _____ days

   b) estimate the approximate time it would take to count from 1 to 1 billion.

      (i) _____ days

      (ii) _____ years

2. Do you think you could count one number every second? If not, why and how long do you think it would take? Use this new estimate to arrive at the approximate number of years it would take to count to one billion if you did not need to stop for food or sleep.

3. Make reasonable assumptions about:
   - the average number of times your heart beats in a minute, and
   - the number of years you expect to live.
     Then estimate how many times your own heart will beat in your lifetime.

   (Adapted from Kelly, B. (1999). "Number Sense & Numeration". Toronto, Ontario. Ministry of Education & Training.)

Refer to Page 123 for the answers

Multiplication tables

An investigation for Primary 3 and Primary 4

"Think of a number from 1 to 10.

Multiply this number by 9.

If the result is a 2-digit number, add the digits together.

Now subtract 5.

Determine which letter in the alphabet corresponds to the number you ended up with (example: 1=a, 2=b, 3=c, 4=d etc.).

Think of a country that starts with that letter.

Remember the last letter in the name of that country.

Think of the name of an animal that starts with that letter."

Investigate:

1. Did you end up with the letter 'd'? Why?

    Hint: Look at the products in the 9 times table.
    $9 \times 1 = 9$
    $9 \times 2 = 18$
    $9 \times 3 = 27$
    $9 \times 4 = 36$
    $9 \times 5 = 45$
    $9 \times 6 = 54$
    $9 \times 7 = 63$
    $9 \times 8 = 72$
    $9 \times 9 = 81$

2. Write down the 2, 3, 4, 5, 6, 7, 8 times tables and observe the products in each of them.
    If the product is a 2-digit number, add up the digits together.
    Do you observe the pattern in the products in each times table?

Addition and subtraction with sticks

- Have you seen the numbers on a digital clock before? Do you realise that these numbers are made up of straight lines?

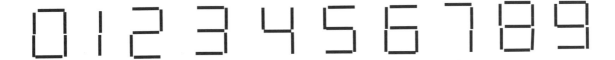

The following mathematical statements are incorrect.
Make them correct by moving one stick in each of them.

1. $9 - 8 = 15$

2. $1 + 1 = 6$

3. $99 - 59 = 10$

The following mathematical statements are incorrect.
Make them correct by moving two sticks in each of them.

4. $19 - 7 = 8$

5. $23 + 16 = 88$

Refer to Page 123 for the answers

Knowing your country

- The following worksheet integrates NE and number sense. Pupils will get to know Singapore better as they complete the worksheet.

Select the numbers that best fit the facts. Then fill in the blanks. Justify your selection.

Singapore, My Country, My Home

7.7	14	23	29	42
63	77	146	150	648
1819	1965	1979	3 870 000	

Singapore is made up of one main island and about _____ smaller ones. The main island spans _____ km from east to west and _____ km from north to south. The total land area is about _____ sq. km, half of which is heavily built up.

Sir Stamford Raffles first set foot in Singapore on the afternoon of _____ January _____. He found about _____ people living along the river banks. _____ years later, in the year _____ , Singapore became an independent state.

Today, the population of Singapore is about _____. About _____ % of the population are Chinese, _____ % Malays and _____ % Indians. There are also Eurasian, Arab and European communities in Singapore. All the different communities live harmoniously together and call Singapore home.

In _____, the Courtesy Campaign was introduced to make Singapore an even warmer and friendlier place to live and work in.

- You may wish to check your answers at this website: http//www.sg.

Refer to Page 124 for the answers

3-D visualisation

A polyhedron is a solid, such as the cube and regular tetrahedron given below. The faces of a polyhedron are polygons. An edge is the segment common to two faces. A vertex is a point common to three or more faces. The cube and the regular tetrahedron shown below have been truncated by passing a plan through the solids, cutting off a vertex of each.

1. Test your visualisation skills. State tell how many vertices (V), faces (F) and edges (E) can be found on the regular tetrahedron and on each truncated polyhedron.

Cube	Truncated Cube	Regular Tetrahedron	Truncated Tetrahedron

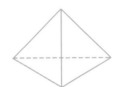
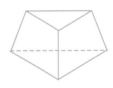

a) V = _8_   b) V = ___   c) V = ___   d) V = ___

F = _6_   F = ___   F = ___   F = ___

E = _12_   E = ___   E = ___   E = ___

2. Now imagine that each and every vertex of the cube and of the tetrahedron is cut off by passing a plan through the midpoints of the three adjacent edges. Can you 'see' the resulting solids? How many vertices, faces and edges are on each?

a) Remains of the cube: V = ___,   F = ___,   E = ___.

b) Remains of the regular tetrahedron: V = ___,   F = ___,   E = ___.

****

The formula below shows the relationship among the vertices (v), edges (e) and faces (f) of a closed polyhedron. It was discovered by the mathematician Descartes in the seventeen century.

$$v - e + f = 2$$

You may use it to verify your results.

(Adapted from 'Teaching with student math notes' by Evan M. Maletsky, NCTM 1987.)

Refer to Page 125 for the answers

Alphabet symmetry

- The objective of this exercise is to provide experiences for exploration of symmetry.

- You will need to prepare a worksheet with all the 26 capital letters of the alphabet. Look at the letters below. Some of them have symmetry.

A B C D E F

G H I J K L

M N O P Q R

S T U V W X

Y Z

1. Which letters have symmetry? Draw the line(s) of symmetry on the symmetric figures.

2. Some letters can be used to form a word that has symmetry, e.g.

HIDE ········· line of symmetry

Form 5 more words that have symmetry.

Symmetry

- This exercise provides experiences for exploration of symmetry.

- You will need paper symmetrical shapes as drawn below. (You may find more of these shapes in the computer software, Word 97/AutoShapes.)

1. Give pupils one shape at a time. Let them experiment with folding the shapes until the halves match.

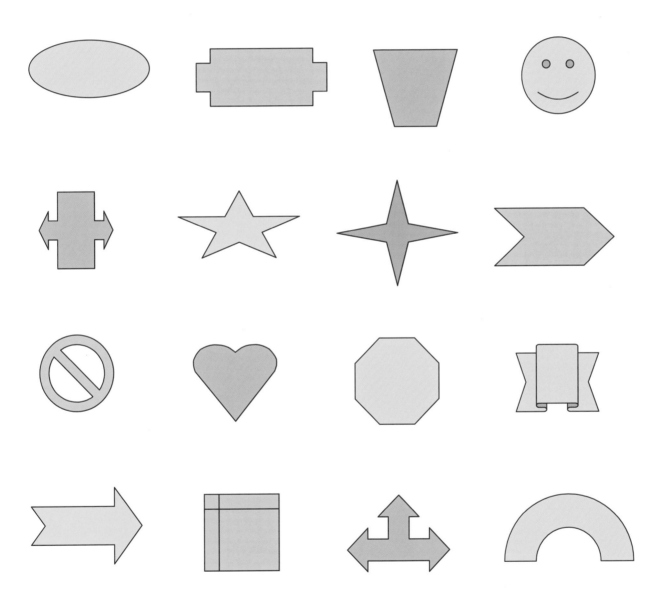

2. Provide pupils with paper squares and rectangles. Show them how they can fold the shapes in the middle and cut the sides to come up with some symmetrical shapes.

Making shapes on a geoboard

An investigation activity for Primary 2

- What you will need:
  A 25-pin geoboard, rubber bands, worksheet and pencil.

1. Make a 3-sided figure on the geoboard.

2. What is the shape? _____

3. What is the largest triangle you can make?

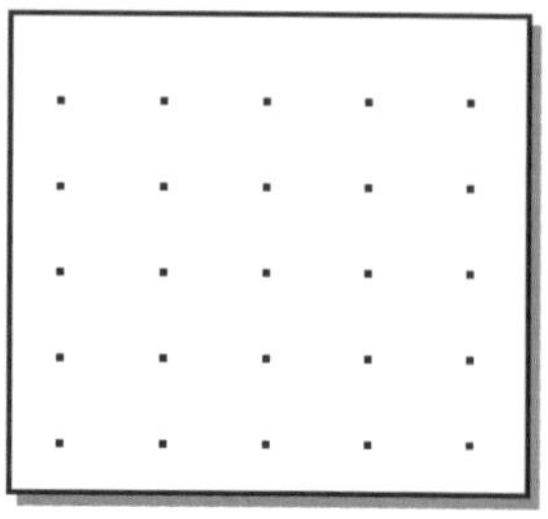

4. What is the smallest triangle you can make?
   How many triangles of this size can you make?

   _____

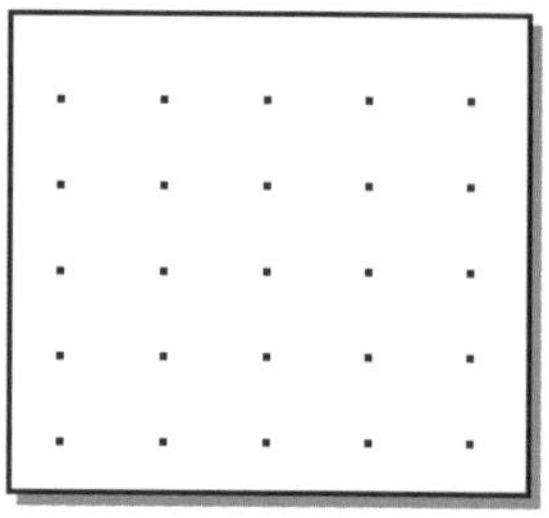

5. How many different triangular shapes can you make?
   Record them below.

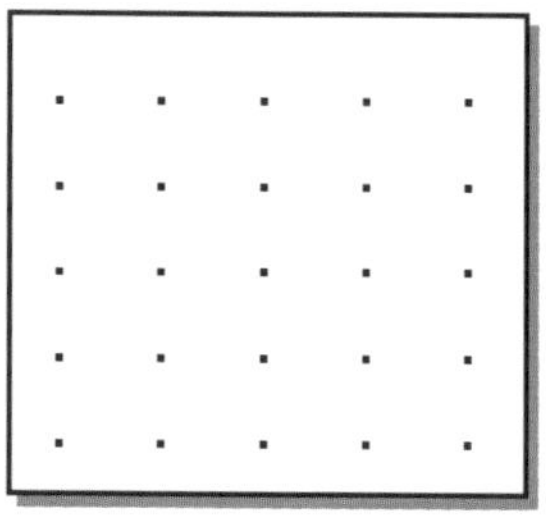

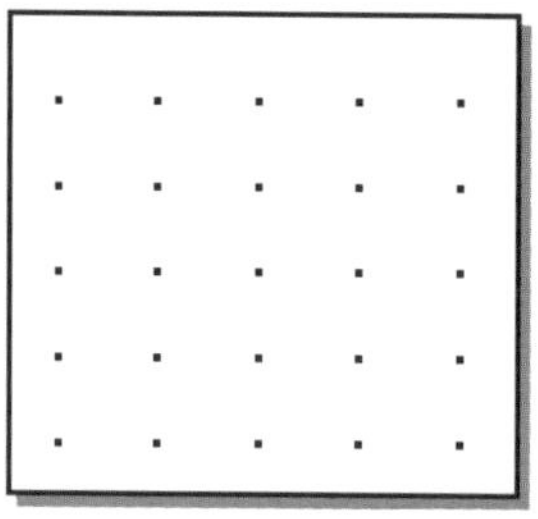

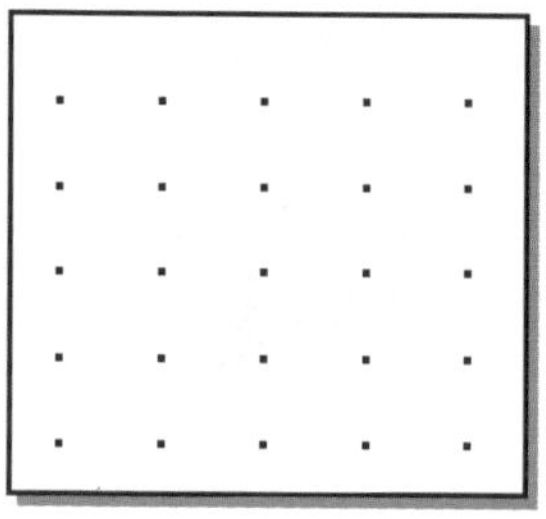

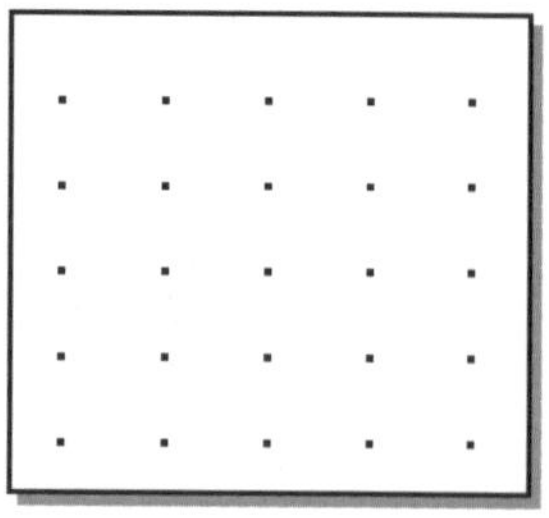

Investigate for squares.
How many squares of different sizes can you make? _____

Counting squares and rectangles

1. Count the number of squares and rectangles in the square arrays and complete the table below:

Array	Figure	(A) Draw all squares No. of squares	(B) Draw all rectangles No. of rectangles	(C) Total (A+ B)
1 × 1	☐	☐ (1)	— (0)	1
2 × 2		( )	( )	
3 × 3		( )	( )	

2. a) Compare the numbers in column (A). Do you observe a pattern? Write it down.

   b) Compare the numbers in column (C). Do you observe another pattern? Write it down.

   c) Use the patterns you have observed to predict the number of squares and rectangles of all sizes in a 4 × 4 array. Verify your answer by counting the squares and rectangles.

   d) A 49-pin geoboard is a 6 × 6 array of squares. How many squares of all sizes does it contain? How many rectangles of all sizes does it contain?

(Adapted from 'Teaching with student math notes' by Evan M. Maletsky, NCTM 1987.)

Refer to Page 125 for the answers

Open-ended and non-routine problem-solving

Story telling

1. "4 × 5 = 20"

   Tell a story sum that will use the above statement for the solution.
   Explain with diagrams the answer to your story sum.

Colours

2. Mr Ali wants to paint his bookshelf with 2 different colours. He has a choice of 8 different colours. In how many ways can he choose the 2 colours to paint his bookshelf?

Money

3. Jean and Mary each had 3 kinds of coins: 10-cent, 20-cent and 50-cent. Mary had 10 coins. She added up the value of the coins and found that she had $2.50. Jean counted her coins and found that she had 2 more 50-cent coins and some more 10-cent and 20-cent coins than Mary. If altogether she had $4.10, how many 10-cent and 20-cent coins had she more than Mary? What were the coins that Jean had?

Fast food

4. The teacher in-charge of a school camp is working out her food order. She likes to make fries and knows that they are a favourite with most children. She calculates that she will need 49 kg of potatoes to feed everyone. When she goes to the store to buy the potatoes she finds that they are already packed and come in either 3-kg or 5-kg bags. She does not want to buy any more than 49 kg. How many 3-kg and 5-kg bags should she get in order to get the exact amount she needs?

Bells

5. The workers of a community centre installed a bell on the clock at the top of the building so that it chimed on the hour. They were pleased that it sounded so impressive. But soon the residents living nearby were complaining. "Do you know how many times a day I have to listen to that bell?" complained one resident. Work out how many times a day the bell chimed.

Concert tickets

6. A school choir was organising a concert in a small concert hall that had 100 seats. All tickets were sold out on the first night and they raised $98. On the second night, all tickets were also sold out, but this time they raised $132.50. For both nights, the tickets were sold at $2 for adults and 50 cents for children. When the choir members were checking the money collected, they could not work out why more money was collected on the second night when the same number of tickets were sold for both nights. What might be the reason for this?

Buying souvenirs

7.   You are left with $5 to spend at the souvenir shop at the Bird Park. You want
     to buy something for your friends. The items you are interested in are:

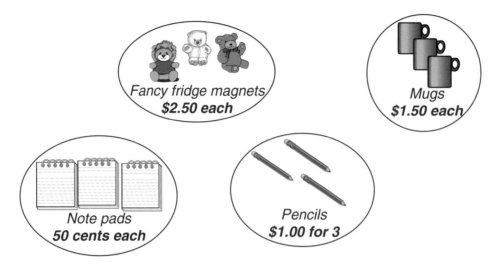

Fancy fridge magnets
$2.50 each

Mugs
$1.50 each

Note pads
50 cents each

Pencils
$1.00 for 3

You make up your mind finally. When you leave the shop, you have spent all
your money. What might be the things that you have bought?

Football T-shirts

8. The captain of a football team bought new T-shirts for his members. He found that these T-shirts had no numbers on the back. He asked his members to make it themselves. But he only had labels with single digits of the following numbers: 1, 2, 3 and 5. Could they use these labels to make enough different numbers (of less than 100) so that a set of 18 T-shirts could be ready for the first match?

Salary

9. Wai Cheng is offered a part-time job in a 7-day Education Conference. Her job is to receive orders and to issue photographs to the conference participants. Her boss gives her a choice as to how she could be paid:

$100 for the seven days

OR

$1 the first day, $2 the second day, $4 the third day and so on, doubling the money each day up to seven days

If Wai Cheng asks you to help her to decide, which choice will you advise her to take? Why?

Calculator

10. If the [5] key on your calculator were broken, how would you do this problem?

$$458 + 548 + 354 = \ ?$$

Write down the steps you would use.

Fencing

11. A rectangular garden is to be fenced off using the wall as one of its sides. If the total length of fencing to be used is 60 m, what dimensions will give the largest area to be enclosed?
(The dimensions are in whole numbers.)

117

Parking charges

12. Mr Wong and his family arrived at a car park in a shopping centre at 3.45 pm. Mr and Mrs Wong went shopping while their daughter went for her dancing class. They met again later and had dinner at a restaurant in the same building. How much parking fees did Mr Wong pay for that outing?

P Parking Charges	From 8.00 a.m. to 5.00 p.m.	First $\frac{1}{2}$ hour	$1.00
		Subsequent hour	$1.50 per hour
	After 5.00 p.m.	—	$2.00 per entry

Answers to Enrichment Activities

Throw the rings!

A practice activity for addition of three numbers

1. 1+1+8, 1+2+7, 1+3+6, 1+4+5, 2+2+6, 2+3+5, 2+4+4, 3+3+4

2. 1+4+10, 1+5+9, 1+6+8, 1+7+7,
   2+3+10, 2+4+9, 2+5+8, 2+6+7,

   3+3+9, 3+4+8, 3+5+7, 3+6+6,
   4+4+7. 4+5+6. 5+5+5

3. 30

4. 3

5. 3, 6, 9, 12, 15, 18, 21, 24, 27, 30

6. 2 or 8

Triangular numbers & square numbers

1

Position n^{th}	Triangular numbers T_n	Sum	Square numbers S_n	Product/sum of triangular numbers
1st	1	1 = 1	1	$1 = 1 \times 1 = 1$
2nd	3	3 = 1 + 2	4	$4 = 2 \times 2 = 1 + 3$
3rd	6	6 = 1 + 2 + 3	9	$9 = 3 \times 3 = 3 + 6$
4th	10	10= 1 + 2 + 3 + 4	16	$16 = 4 \times 4 = 6 + 10$
5th	15	15= 1 + 2 + 3 + 4 + 5	25	$25 = 5 \times 5 = 10 + 15$
6th	21	21= 1 + 2 + 3 + 4 + 5 + 6	36	$36 = 6 \times 6 = 15 + 21$

2. 10th Triangular number = 1 + 2 + 3 + 4 + 5 = + 6 + 7 + 8 + 9 + 10
   $$= 55$$
   10th Square number $= 10 \times 10$
   $$= 100$$

3. $T_n = 1 + 2 + 3 + 4 + \ldots\ldots\ldots +n$ (or $= \frac{n(n+1)}{2}$)

   $S_n = n^2$

4. $S_n = T_{n-1} + T_n$

119

Arranging chairs

1. 6

    $1 \times 12, 2 \times 6, 3 \times 4, 4 \times 3, 6 \times 2, 12 \times 1$

2. $1 \times 6, 2 \times 3, 3 \times 2, 6 \times 1$

3. $1 \times 7, 7 \times 1$

4. Complete the table.

No. of chairs	No. of rows		No. of chairs in a row		Kind of no.*
6	1		6		
	2		3		Composite number
	3		2		
	6		1		
7	1		7		Prime number
	7		1		
8	1		8		
	2		4		Composite number
	4		2		
	8		1		
9	1		9		
	3		3		Square number
	9		1		
10	1		10		
	2		5		Composite number
	5		2		
	10		1		
11	1		11		Prime number
	11		1		
12	1	12	12	1	
	2	6	6	2	Composite number
	3	4	4	3	
13	1		13		Prime number
	13		1		
14	1		14		
	2		7		Composite number
	7		2		
	14		1		
15	1		15		
	3		5		Composite number
	5		3		
	15		1		
16	1		16		
	2		8		
	4		4		Square number
	8		2		
	16		1		
17	1		17		Prime number
	17		1		
18	1	18	18	1	
	2	9	9	2	Composite number
	3	6	6	3	
19	1		19		Prime number
	19		1		
20	1	20	20	1	
	2	10	10	2	
	4		5		Composite number
	5		4		

5. 7, 11, 13, 17, 19

6. 9, 16

120

How long would it take you to count to one billion?

1a) (i) 1 000 000 seconds

(ii) 16 666.666 minutes

(iii) 277.777 hours

(iv) 11.574 days

b) (i) 11 574 days

(ii) 31.7 years

Addition and subtraction with sticks

1. 9 + 8 = 15

2. 7 + 1 = 6

3. 89 − 59 = 10

4. 19 − 17 = 8

5. 93 + 16 = 88

Knowing your country

- The following worksheet integrates NE and number sense. Pupils will get to know Singapore better as they complete the worksheet.

Select the numbers that best fit the facts. Then fill in the blanks. Justify your selection.

Singapore,
My Country, My Home

7.7	14	23	29	42
63	77	146	150	648
1819	1965	1979	3 870 000	

Singapore is made up of one main island and about ___63___ smaller ones. The main island spans ___42___ km from east to west and ___23___ km from north to south. The total land area is about ___648___ sq. km, half of which is heavily built up.

Sir Stamford Raffles first set foot in Singapore on the afternoon of ___29___ January ___1819___. He found about ___150___ people living along the river banks. ___146___ years later, in the year ___1965___, Singapore became an independent state.

Today, the population of Singapore is about _3 870 000_. About ___77___ % of the population are Chinese, ___14___ % Malays and ___7.7___ % Indians. There are also Eurasian, Arab and European communities in Singapore. All the different communities live harmoniously together and call Singapore home.

In ___1979___, the Courtesy Campaign was introduced to make Singapore an even warmer and friendlier place to live and work in.

3-D visualisation

1a)   ----
  b)   V = 10, F = 7, E = 15
  c)   V = 4,   F = 4, E = 6
  d)   V = 6,   F = 5, E = 9

2a)   V = 12, F = 14, E = 24
  b)   V = 12, F = 8,   E = 18

Counting squares and rectangles

1. 1×1: (A) 1, (B) 1, (C) I; 2×2: (A) 5, (B) 4, (C) 9; 3×3: (A) 14, (B) 22, (C) 36

2 a) $1 = 1 = 1^2$, $5 = 1 + 4 = 1^2 + 2^2$, $14 = 1 + 4 + 9 = 1^2 + 2^2 + 3^2$

  b) $1 = 1 = 1^3$, $9 = 1 + 8 = 1^3 + 2^3$, $36 = 1 + 8 + 27 = 1^3 + 2^3 + 3^3$

  c)   Number of squares = 30
       Number of rectangles = 70

  d)   Number of squares = 91
       Number of rectangles = 350

Assessment and Test Construction

"Assessment is the process of gathering information about children in order to make decisions about their education. Teachers obtain useful information about children's knowledge, skills and progress by observing, documenting and reviewing children's work over time. Ongoing assessment that occurs in the context of classroom activities can provide an accurate, fair and representative picture of children's abilities and progress." *(Dodge, Jablon & Bickart, 1994)*

"Assessment involves the multiple steps of collecting data on a child's development and learning, determining its significance in light of the program goals and objectives, incorporating the information into planning for individuals and programs, and communicating the findings to parents and other involved parties." *(Hills, 1992)*

ASSESSMENT IN MATHEMATICS

- **Assessment methods**
- **Construction of test/examination paper**
- **Table of specifications**
- **General principles of writing test items**
- **Types of test items (with examples)**
- **Checklist for editing items**
- **General principles of marking**

1.1 ASSESSMENT METHODS

Traditional assessments

- Pupils choose a response from a given list. Examples of these test items are:

    — multiple-choice,
    — true-false, and
    — matching.

- Other item-types provide teachers with better understanding of pupils' abilities and progress. Examples are:

    — short answer questions,
    — problems,
    — tasks, and
    — investigations that can vary from focused to open-ended.

Alternative assessments

- Pupils can demonstrate their thinking and understanding in other ways, such as:

    — written reports or journals,
    — oral presentations,
    — exhibitions (constructed models and materials),
    — project work, and
    — portfolios.

1.2 CONSTRUCTION OF TEST/EXAMINATION PAPER

Objectives of classroom test

- To diagnose pupils' strengths and weaknesses, to identify what has or has not been learnt by pupils so that planning and correction can be done
- To monitor pupils' progress
- To evaluate pupils and assign grades or marks to show parents what pupils have achieved
- To evaluate the effectiveness of the teaching programme

Setting the paper

- Study the syllabus content to determine the important outcomes to be assessed
- Determine the format of the paper
- Work out a Table of Specifications (TOS)
- Write the questions together with the answer key/marking scheme
- Take the test yourself or ask a colleague to take the test (under test conditions)
- Multiply the amount of time taken to complete the test by 3 to obtain the approximate amount of time pupils will need to complete the test
- Revise and polish the paper
- Edit the questions before administering the test

1.3 TABLE OF SPECIFICATIONS (TOS)

Determine the relative weightings for the topics to be assessed

- List the topics to be tested and the amount of teaching time allotted to each of them.
- Compute the relative weighting as a % using the formula:

$$\text{Relative weighting} = \frac{\text{Teaching time per topic}}{\text{Total teaching time}} \times 100\,\%$$

Topic	Time per topic	Relative weighting
Total		100 %

- A template for the Table of Specifications is given in **Annex AST–1**.

- You can refer to the following example on how to plan a TOS for Primary Three.

Example

Plan a Table of Specifications based on the following Scheme of Work.

(A sample scheme of work (SOW) for P3 Term I is given below.)

- List the Scheme of Work for the term.

Week 1	Whole numbers
Week 2	Whole numbers
Week 3	Whole numbers
Week 4	Whole numbers
Week 5	Fractions
Week 6	Fractions
Week 7	Length
Week 8	Weight
Week 9	Continuous Assessment 1
Week 10	Money

- Using the formula as a guide, calculate an approximate relative weighting of the topic for the Continuous Assessment 1.

	Topic	Time per topic	Relative weighting
1	Whole numbers	4 weeks	$\frac{4}{8}$ x 100 % = 50%
2	Fractions	2 weeks	$\frac{2}{8}$ x 100 % = 25%
3	Length	1 week	$\frac{1}{8}$ x 100 % = 12.5%
4	Weight	1 week	$\frac{1}{8}$ x 100 % = 12.5%
Total		8 weeks	100%

Determine the format of the paper

Section A: Multiple-choice	20 items	No. 1 – 10 @ 1 mark No. 11 – 20 @ 2 marks	30 marks
Section B: Open-ended (Short-answer)	20 items	No. 21 – 40 @ 2 marks	40 marks
Section C: Problem sums (Structured/Long-answer)	8 items	No. 41 – 42 @ 3 marks No. 43 – 48 @ 4 marks	30 marks
Total	48 items		100 marks

Work out roughly the number of questions for each topic

- Use the formula:

No. of questions per topic $= \dfrac{\text{Relative weighting of topic}}{\text{Total weighting}} \times$ Total number of questions per section

> ### *Example*
>
> For the topic on whole numbers (from the example given earlier):
>
> Section A
> Whole numbers — 50% of 20 questions — 10 questions
>   — 50% of 30 marks — 15 marks
>
> Section B
> Whole numbers — 50% of 20 questions — 10 questions
>   — 50% of 40 marks — 20 marks
>
> Section C
> Whole numbers — 50% of 8 questions — 4 questions
>   — 50% of 30 marks — 15 marks
>
> Total number of questions for whole numbers — 24 questions
> Total marks allotted for whole numbers   — 50 marks

Determine the weightings of each cognitive domain for each topic

- 'Knowledge' refers to the ability to recall specific mathematical facts, concepts, rules and formulae, and to perform straightforward computations.

- 'Comprehension' refers to the ability to interpret data and use a mathematical concept, rule or formula in an essentially familiar situation.

- 'Application'/'Higher-order' refers to the ability to analyse data and/or to apply a mathematical concept, rule or formula in a complex situation or to an unfamiliar problem.

- Express the weightings of each cognitive domain for each topic as a % and indicate the number of questions to be set at 'K', 'C' and 'A' for each topics.

- The weighting for the cognitive levels may vary based on the objectives of the test and the professional judgement of the setter.

(Examples of questions assessing the different cognitive levels and examples of non-routine/unfamiliar questions are given in **Annex AST–2**.)

1.4 GENERAL PRINCIPLES OF WRITING TEST ITEMS

1.4.1 Stages of item preparation

Writing

— Always look out for suitable items. Keep a 'question notebook' to note down ideas, especially during lesson preparation and teaching.
— When noting down items, include acceptable answers and a tentative mark scheme.

Presentation

— It is easier for pupils to read quickly and understand what is required if an item is arranged systematically. Good presentation and organisation guide pupils and allow answers to be marked quickly and accurately.

Editing (or vetting)

— Other teachers should be asked to vet both the content and the construction of items. They should work out answers without reference to the writer's answers and cross check the solutions and mark scheme.
— They should also check for ambiguity and give alternative solutions and mark schemes.

First use

— Ideally, all items should be trialled and tested.
— In practice, a teacher is unable to do this. A more realistic approach is to use the information obtained from the first real use of the items to write future items.

Performance

— Review items and pupils' answers to note ambiguities, poor appraisal distractors and pupils' performance. The best check of an item is how well it worked in practice as revealed by the pupils' answers.

Reviewing

— Review items before storing them in an item bank for future use. Base your review on content, effectiveness of purpose, facility index (difficulty level) and discriminative index (high/average/low discrimination).

Storage or banking

— Use a proper and clear cataloguing system to keep 'good' items for future use.
— While you may not want to repeat an entire question, you may want to change the numbers used while keeping the phrasing or the original idea of the question intact.

1.4.2 Note the following when setting items

- <u>Test only</u> relevant and important things.

- <u>Avoid ambiguity</u>. <u>Set specific tasks</u>. Give clear instructions.

- <u>Be brief </u>and ask <u>direct</u> questions as far as possible. Try to have only 1 main idea in each sentence.

- Use <u>simple language</u>.

- <u>Avoid negatively worded items or stems</u> — where a negative is unavoidable, emphasise by underlining or highlighting the negative words (examples of negative words are none, no, not, except, etc.).

- As far as possible, the next part of an item <u>should not depend on an answer</u> found in an earlier part. The penalty will be severe for pupils who make mistakes in the earlier part but know how to solve the latter part.

- Check that <u>items do not give clues</u> to solving other items in the same test.

- When using names of several people or places, try to use them in <u>alphabetical order</u> to reduce confusion, and to make it easier to read and remember.

- Leave <u>sufficient space</u> for working and answers. For completion items and items with blanks, leave enough space to accommodate variations in handwriting.

- Arrange items so that it will <u>not</u> be <u>necessary</u> for pupils <u>to refer to more than one page</u> for each question.

- <u>Do not place blanks at the beginning</u> of sentences. Use at most only 2 blanks in an item. All blanks should be of the same length. If a blank in an item requires an answer with units, specify the units unless the aim of the item is to test units.

- Indicate the <u>relative weighting</u> of each part of the question where possible.

1.5 TYPES OF TEST ITEMS

Let us now look at four types of test items commonly used in primary schools. There will be a brief description of each type followed by more specific ideas.

• **Matching items**
• **Multiple-choice questions**
• **Short-answer items**
• **Problem sums**

1.5.1 Matching items

Description

- Tests knowledge only
- Is used to determine whether pupils can discriminate between similar ideas or facts
- Consists of 2 parallel lists that require pupils to match one list with another
- Deals with common items of a single category
- Is usually fun for pupils, especially if there are pictures or diagrams
- Easy to mark

Specific ideas about matching items

- Place the list containing the shorter words or phrases on the right.
- Entries on the right should be ordered in a logical manner.
- More entries could be placed on the right than on the left in order to reduce chances for guessing.
- Have a maximum of 10 entries as too many entries would waste pupils' time in searching for the correct match.
- Tell pupils what they have to do, e.g. draw a line, label, etc.

Example 1

On the line of each percentage listed in Column I, write the letter of the fraction that is equal to it. Each fraction in Column II may be used only once.

Column I

1. 90% = _____

2. 40% = _____

3. 25% = _____

Column II

(a) $\dfrac{1}{4}$

(b) $\dfrac{1}{2}$

(c) $\dfrac{2}{5}$

(d) $\dfrac{4}{6}$

(e) $\dfrac{9}{10}$

Comments

- Note that the fraction given in Distractor (d) is not in the lowest term. All fractions in the options should be expressed in the lowest term unless the objective is to identify equivalent fractions.

Example 2

Choose the best match between the numbers in List A and the expressions in List B.

List A

1. 115

2. 105

3. 150

List B

(a) $100 + 5$
(b) 100×15
(c) $100 + 50$
(d) $100 + 15$
(e) $100 \div 5$

Comments

- This question is ambiguous. What does 'best match' mean?
- The questions that need to be worked out should be placed on the left and the answers should be placed on the right.
- The instruction does not tell pupils what they have to do, e.g. draw a line.
- The items in List B deal with items belonging to three different ideas — addition, division and multiplication. When put together in one question, this may be confusing for pupils.
- All the correct answers are for the additions. It is obvious that (b) and (e) are redundant.

1.5.2 Multiple-Choice Items

Description

- Consists of 3 parts:
  - i) a stem — the part that precedes the options, i.e. the 'question'
  - ii) a key — the correct option
  - iii) distractors — plausible but incorrect options
- Easy to mark and analyse
- Allows for guessing, sometimes clues are given

Specific ideas about multiple-choice items

- Avoid giving clues in the stem and options. Make sure that the options follow the stem grammatically.
- If the same word or words appear in all the options, consider putting them in the stem. As much of the item as possible should be included in the item stem.
- This format could be used when teachers want to limit the pupils' choice of answers (e.g. question on factors or multiples) or do not want pupils to bother with spelling or naming (e.g. naming a line parallel to a given line).
- Distractors should arise from common misconceptions and mistakes, and not from careless mistakes arising from calculations.
- When the distractor is hard to come by, the item should not be set as a multiple-choice item.
- Avoid using 'one of the above' and 'all of the above' as options.
- Arrange numerical options in ascending or descending order. Match the answer 1 with the option (1), 2 with (2), etc. even if this disrupts the ascending or descending order of the rest of the options. This is easier for pupils to read.
- Every item should have only one correct answer.
- Options should be parallel in structure. Maintain item-length similarity and make sure the options look 'balanced'.

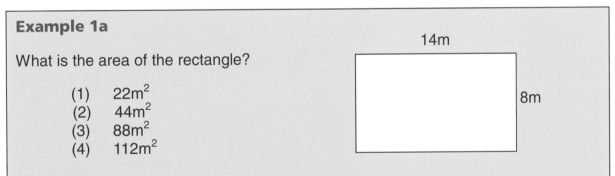

Example 1a

What is the area of the rectangle?

    (1)   22m^2
    (2)   44m^2
    (3)   88m^2
    (4)   112m^2

14m

8m

Comments

- (1) is obtained from adding the two numbers together.
- (2) is obtained from finding the perimeter. This is a common error.
- (3) is obtained from multiplying (1) by 4.
- (4) is the key. It is the only 3-digit number so it may give away clues to pupils. Change the dimensions of the rectangle to make the options more balanced.
- Since the unit is repeated for all the options, the item may be written as a fill-in-the blank item with the unit in the stem rather than in the options as shown in (1b).

Example 1b

The area of the rectangle is _____ m^2.

    (1)   27
    (2)   54
    (3)   108
    (4)   162

18m

9m

Example 2

Which of the following is a factor of 28?

    (1)   56
    (2)   9
    (3)   3
    (4)   4

Comments

- (1) is a multiple of 28 which is a common error. However, it is the only distractor where the number is a rather large 2-digit number.
- (2) and (3) seem to be possible answers at first glance.
- The options are not parallel in structure. They should be re-written as '(1) 56 (2) 36 (3) 3 (4) 4' to give 2 pairs of parallel structure.
- Note that the number 3 is matched with option (3) and the number 4 with option (4).

Example 3

Which of the following is a multiple of 8?
    (1)   12
    (2)   24
    (3)   32
    (4)   45

Comments

- Though the distractors have the same length, i.e. all are two-digit numbers, these are poor distractors overall. The numbers are all greater than 8 and there are no factors. Pupils who are confused between factors and multiples can guess the answer. There should be exactly one factor and one multiple in the options as in Example 2.
- The options could be re-written as:
  -     (1)   100
  -     (2)   56
  -     (3)   36
  -     (4)   4
- Though they are not the same length, having 1-digit, 2-digit and 3-digit numbers will reduce chances of guessing.

Example 4

At a party on Sunday, Angelina Koh received 30 sweets. She gave $\frac{2}{5}$ of her sweets to her friends. How many sweets did she have left?

    (1) 6
    (2) 18
    (3) 12
    (4) 75

Comments

- The options should be arranged in ascending order, as in:

    (1) 6
    (2) 12
    (3) 18
    (4) 75

  or in descending order, as in:

    (1) 75
    (2) 18
    (3) 12
    (4) 6

- (1) is the only 1-digit number and it is obtained from $30 \div 5$ which is unlikely to be chosen by pupils. '50' which is $30 \div \frac{3}{5}$ is more likely to be taken as an answer.

- There is no need to use a long name such as Angelina Koh or to lengthen the sentence with "At a party on Sunday". Questions should be placed in context but the resulting sentences should not be too long or complicated.

Example 5

28 x 73 is about _____.

    (1) 1 400
    (2) 1 750
    (3) 2 100
    (4) 2 500

Comments

- Though the distractors are parallel, i.e. all are four-digit numbers, overall they are poor distractors. For an item which tests estimation, the important idea should be the approximate size of the outcome. All the four options given are acceptable estimates.
- The options may be re-written as:

    (1) 210
    (2) 2 100
    (3) 21 000
    (4) 210 000

The numbers have different lengths but they are still considered to be parallel in structure.

Example 6

_____= 123 + 987

    (1)   1 110
    (2)   10 110
    (3)   11 010
    (4)   101 010

Comments

- The stem should be at the beginning and rewritten as '123 + 987 = _____.'
- Blanks should not be placed at the beginning of an item. If there is no other way of placing the blank, rephrase the entire question.
- This particular item should be re-set using the short-answer format. Here, the distractors may not include the pupils' answers and this gives them clues regarding whether answers are correct or incorrect.

Example 7a

The number of tens in 54 150 is _____.

    (1)   5
    (2)   15
    (3)   415
    (4)   5 415

Comments

- This item is ambiguous. Which is the answer? 5 or 5 415?
- The item could be re-written as shown below:

Example 7b

In which number does the digit 5 stand for 5 tens?

    (1)   5 678
    (2)   6 578
    (3)   6 758
    (4)   6 785

        OR

    (1)   5 761
    (2)   576
    (3)   57
    (4)   6

1.5.3 Short-answer items

Description

- Pupils supply a word, a short phrase, a number or a symbol that answers a question or completes a sentence.
- Can be a direct question, a sentence completion item or a fill-in-the-blank item. Less guessing and fewer clues compared to multiple-choice items.
- Provides excellent source of distractors for multiple-choice items.
- Best used for measurement of specific knowledge.
- Short-answer items are useful for checking misunderstandings and misconceptions.

Specific ideas about short-answer items

- There should be only one correct answer (with acceptable equivalent answers).
- Answers should be short: a word, a phrase, a number, a symbol or a simple diagram.
- Specify the degree of precision required where necessary.
- If pupils have to supply the unit of measure in their answer, they have to be told to do so in the question.
- If a single, complex item can be divided into parts so that each part resembles a short-answer item, then the item should be treated as a problem sum and not a short-answer item. Short-answer items are generally short and simple items.

Example 1a

$\frac{2}{9} \times 15 = \underline{\hspace{2cm}}$

Comments

- Markers have to note that there are many acceptable answers here:

$3\frac{1}{3}, \frac{10}{3}, \frac{30}{9}, 3.3$

- If markers do not want to accept all the answers given above, the question will have to be more specific. It may be rewritten as follows:

Example 1b

$\frac{2}{9} \times 15 = \underline{\hspace{2cm}}$

Give your answer in the simplest form.

Example 2

Use all the digits 0, 4, and 5 to make the smallest even whole number.

Comments

- Pupils may write 054 as an answer. While 054 is not a whole number, it would invite controversy. It is best to avoid including zeroes when dealing with the smallest value.

Example 3

1 055 *ml* = _____ *l* _____ *ml*

Comments

- The length of the blanks makes it obvious that the first blank should be filled with fewer digits than the second. The two blanks must be of the same length.
- Note that 1055*ml* should be marked wrong and 1.055*l* is a possible answer.

Example 4a

What is the correct time if a watch which is 15 minutes slow indicates 9.55 p.m.?

Answer: _____p.m.

- The vocabulary may be too difficult for primary school pupils. It would be easier if the question was rewritten into more than one sentence, for example:

Example 4b

A watch is 15 minutes slow. If it shows the time as 9.55p.m., what is the correct time?

Answer: _____p.m.

- This question can be made easier for Primary Two pupils if a diagram of a watch or clock face is included.

Example 5

(a)   A packet of salt weighs 400 g.
        What is the total weight of 7 packets of the salt?
        Give your answer in kg and g.

Answer:_____

(b)   A packet of salt weighs 400 g.
        What is the total weight of 7 packets of the salt?

Answer: _____kg _____g

- In question (a), we require pupils to write the units themselves. In question (b), we assume that pupils would fill in both blanks. It would be difficult to mark if pupils give answers such as "0 kg 2800 g" or "2.8 kg 0 g" for (b).
- Question (a) has been more explicitly stated. It is clear that the answer should be given as " Answer: _____kg _____g."

1.5.4 Problem sums

Description

- Useful for measuring higher order thinking skills/cognitive domains.
- Allowing pupils to explain their thinking process and problem-solving heuristics.

Specific ideas about problem sums

- Should provide all the relevant information needed (irrelevant data may be provided where identification of relevant data is part of the test).
- Several short sentences are preferable to one long sentence.
- Cannot have too many of such items in a test because of time constraints.
- Items should be clear and specific about what is required from pupil, e.g. "Give the answer in cm." or "Give the answer as a fraction in the simplest form."
- Use language that is appropriate to the level and tell pupils exactly what to do.

Example 1a
The figure shows a square. A quarter of a circle of radius 7cm was cut off as shown. Find the area and perimeter of the remaining part of the square.

(Take $\pi = \dfrac{22}{7}$)

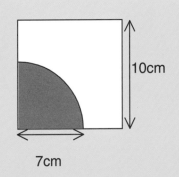

10cm

7cm

Answer:_____

Example 1b
The figure shows a square. A quarter of a circle of radius 7cm was cut off as shown. (Take $\pi = \frac{22}{7}$)

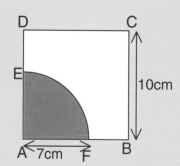

(a) What is the area of the remaining part of the square?
(b) What is the perimeter of the remaining part of the square?

Answer :   (a) _____

              (b) _____

Example 1c
The figure shows a square ABCD. AEF is a quarter of a circle which has a radius of 7cm.
(a) What is the area of the unshaded part BCDEF?

(b) What is the perimeter of the unshaded part BCDEF? (Take $\pi = \frac{22}{7}$)

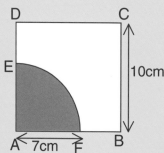

Answer :   (a) _____

              (b) _____

- All three questions are easy to read and understand.
- The format in examples (1a) and (1b) are more helpful to pupils who may forget what the question requires them to do — the two parts labelled (a) and (b) in the answer space remind pupils that there are two parts to be answered.
- Some pupils may not like Example (1c) as they have to check what AEF and BCDEF refer to.

1.6 CHECKLIST FOR EDITING ITEMS

- Is the format of the question (Multiple-choice, Short-answer, Problem-sums) suitable for the items?

Text in question

- Does the text contain the necessary information?
- Is the information realistic/technically accurate?
- Are the words used at a suitable level of difficulty?
- Does the text contain any unfamiliar language or word?
- Is the text written in a clear and concise manner?

Diagram in question

- Does the diagram contain the necessary information?
- Is the diagram clearly labelled?
- Is the diagram consistent with the description accompanying it?
- Is the diagram properly laid out?

Question proper

- Is the question testing a learning outcome similar to another?
- Is the question testing too many ideas?
- Is the question testing trivial knowledge?
- Is the question clear and unambiguous?
- Does the question contain any unfamiliar technical words or symbols?
- Does the question contain any negative word? If so, is it emphasised?

Answer

- Is the instruction on how pupils are expected to give their answers clear?
- Is there more than one way to answer the question? If so, is this acceptable?
- Is the answer dependent on the answers of other questions?

1.7 GENERAL PRINCIPLES OF MARKING

Marking scheme

- Mark positively. Look for things to reward rather than faults to penalise.
- Ask the question. "Is a mark given for a positive response?"
- Check that the responses that are awarded marks are significant for the solution.
- Ensure the mark scheme reflects the amount of work required in each question.
- The marking scheme should be easy to understand and to use.
- Make sure that all markers understand the scheme.

Marking pupils' work

- Do some random sample marking immediately after the test.
- Meet to discuss changes and additions to the marking scheme.
- Mark the rest of the scripts.
- If other problems turn up during marking, note them and discuss them with the other markers before marking the scripts with the problems. All markers should take note of all amendments or decisions made in their marking scheme.

Feedback to pupils

- Ideally, pupils should be aware of how marks are awarded for their work. Teachers may give pupils a rough idea of how their work will be marked to help them prepare for the test.

General principles of marking

- The marking scheme for short-answer items should:
  - list all the acceptable forms of the answer and specify the marks to be awarded.
  - list some unacceptable answers, where necessary.
  - include marks to be awarded for partial answers, partially correct answers and answers which are unsimplified.

- The marking scheme for problem sums should:
  - identify which main points or ideas should be awarded marks (and these should be based on the objective(s) of the question).
  - note where follow-through marks should be awarded for appropriate or correct method shown even though an answer or an intermediate answer is wrong.

> Note that for problem sums:
> - There may be several possible forms of correct answers, e.g. correct but wrongly spelt, correct but poorly drawn, correct but with additional irrelevant material. Markers should agree on the penalty, if any, for such cases.
> - Pupils may omit some or all important working. Markers should agree on the penalty, if any, for such cases.

in IT Skills in Mathematics

This section focusses on some IT skills that are needed to enhance and simplify Mathematics drawings. Some sample IT lesson plans are also provided.

Using IT in Mathematics

1. To show drawing toolbar

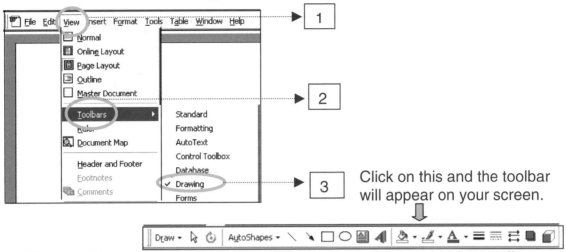

Click on this and the toolbar will appear on your screen.

- You need to use the icons shown on this toolbar to draw autoshapes, lines, etc.

2. To configure measurements in centimetres

- This will enable you to draw diagrams with the exact measurement in centimetres.
- This will automatically help you to fix vertical and horizontal lines at 1cm intervals.

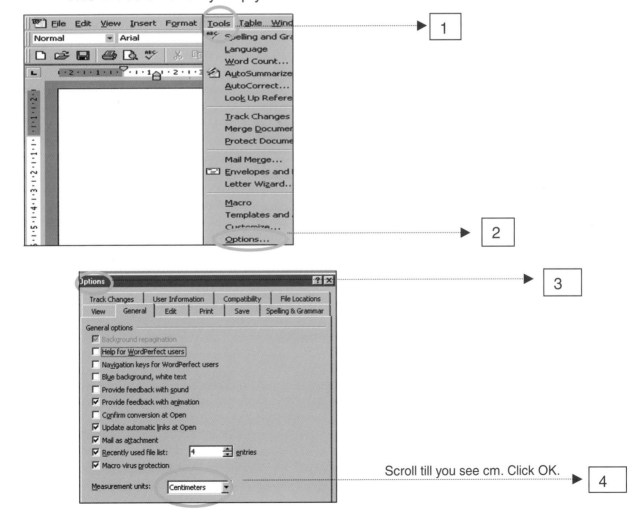

Scroll till you see cm. Click OK.

3. To snap to grid

- This allows a better control of the mouse while drawing.

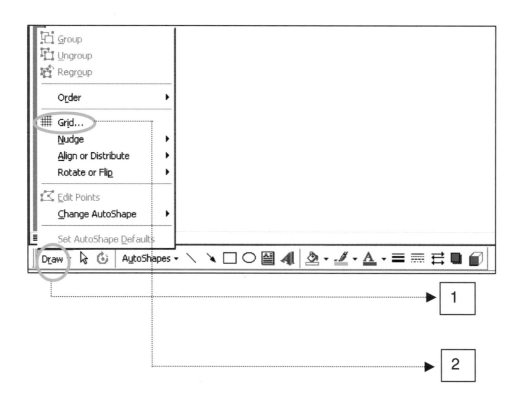

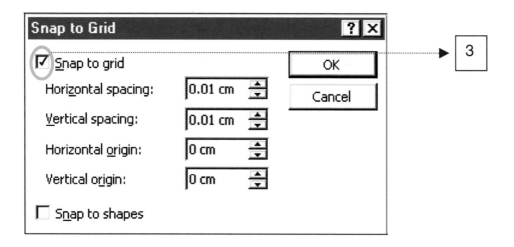

To snap to grid at 1cm vertical height and horizontal height

- This is good for drawing grid lines for area and perimeter diagrams.

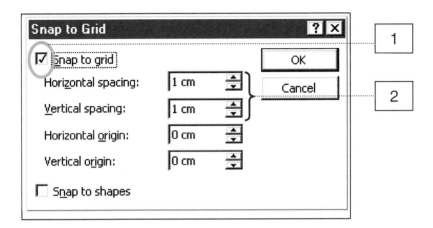

- The horizontal or vertical lines that you draw will be fixed at 1cm intervals.
- You will not be able to draw another line closer than 1 cm.

4. To draw a measured line (eg 5cm line)

- With the configuration in centimetres, you will be able to draw any line measured in cm with this skill.

1   Left click and the cursor will change to a plus sign.

2   Press and hold down the **Shift** key. (This will ensure that the line is horizontal) Drag and pull the plus sign to draw a horizontal line. (Do not worry about the length)

3   Move the cursor to the drawn line and double click on the line. This menu box will appear.

4   Type in the length you want.

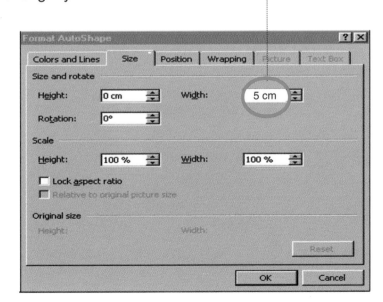

5. To draw a 5cm line that is 30° to the horizontal

- This is very useful for preparing questions on geometry, especially angles.

| 1 | to | 4 | Follow steps 1 to 4 as in exercise (4). Use the same menu box.

| 5 | In the Menu box at Rotation: type 30°
The line will be adjusted to show a 30° slant.

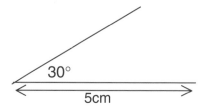

30°
5cm

| 6 | Draw another horizontal line to join up the 5cm line at 30° and you will get an angle of 30°.

6. To create concentric circles

- Draw all the circles in any location.
- Next, select all the circles. To do this, click one circle, then hold down the **Shift** key while you click on the remaining circles. With all the circles selected, click on the **Draw** toolbar and do the following:

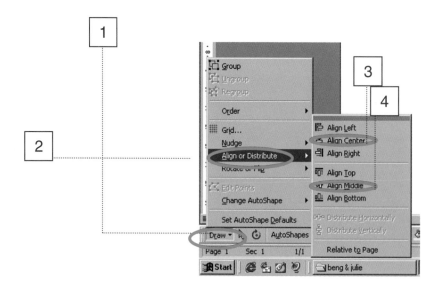

7. To draw circular number discs

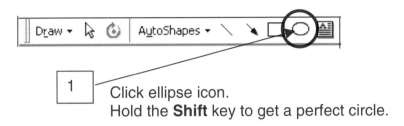

1 Click ellipse icon.
Hold the **Shift** key to get a perfect circle.

- To repeat the disc/circle:

1 Activate the 'circle' you have created (ie. click on the circle).

2 Click to copy at the toolbar.

3 Click to paste the copied item.

- Repeat the actions for multiple copies of the circle.
- Adjust the circles so that they are in the positions that you want.

- To create multiple stacked circles:

1 Put the mouse arrow over the circle.

2 Right mouse click — you'll see this menu-box.

Click **ORDER** — Send to the back.
Do this until the number discs are in the correct order.

- To fill in the numbers in the discs:

1 Insert text box and put into the circle.

2 Right mouse click — **Format Text Box**

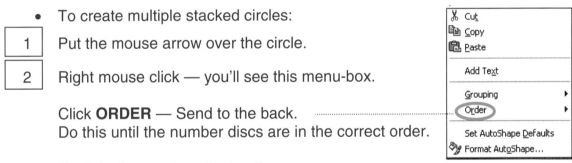

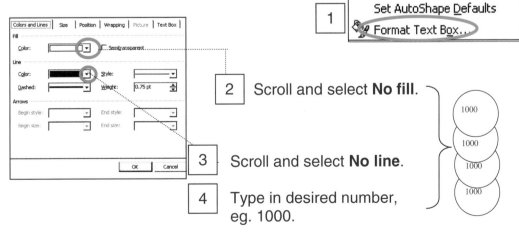

2 Scroll and select **No fill**.

3 Scroll and select **No line**.

4 Type in desired number, eg. 1000.

8. To draw regular mathematical geometric figures

- Ensure that your drawing toolbar is activated to give you this:

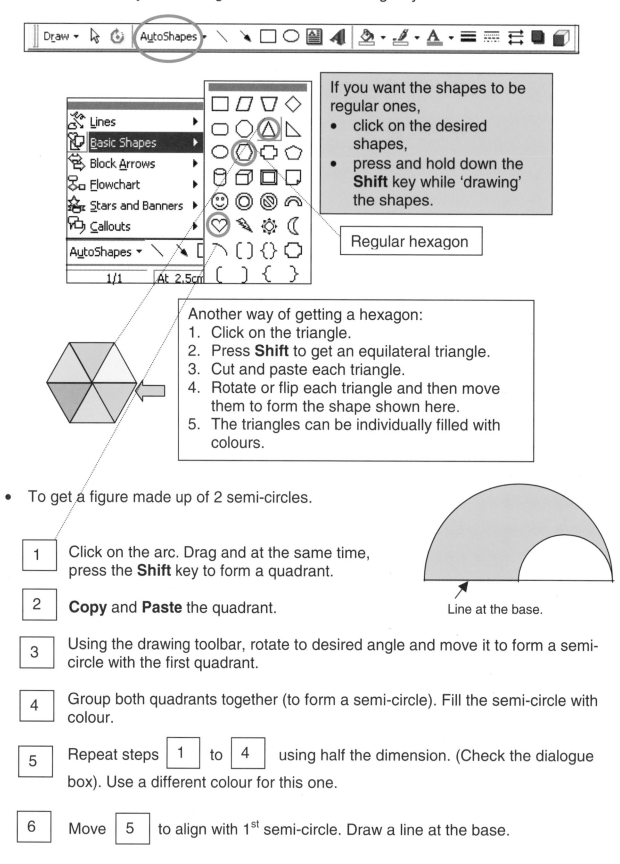

If you want the shapes to be regular ones,
- click on the desired shapes,
- press and hold down the **Shift** key while 'drawing' the shapes.

Regular hexagon

Another way of getting a hexagon:
1. Click on the triangle.
2. Press **Shift** to get an equilateral triangle.
3. Cut and paste each triangle.
4. Rotate or flip each triangle and then move them to form the shape shown here.
5. The triangles can be individually filled with colours.

- To get a figure made up of 2 semi-circles.

| 1 | Click on the arc. Drag and at the same time, press the **Shift** key to form a quadrant. |

| 2 | **Copy** and **Paste** the quadrant. |

Line at the base.

| 3 | Using the drawing toolbar, rotate to desired angle and move it to form a semi-circle with the first quadrant. |

| 4 | Group both quadrants together (to form a semi-circle). Fill the semi-circle with colour. |

| 5 | Repeat steps 1 to 4 using half the dimension. (Check the dialogue box). Use a different colour for this one. |

| 6 | Move 5 to align with 1st semi-circle. Draw a line at the base. |

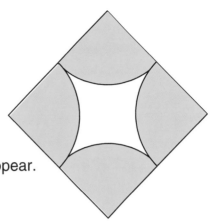

- To shade a circle.
  Activate the drawing toolbar.

1   Click on **Autoshapes**
Basic Shapes
Arc
Move cursor to page and click. A quadrant will appear.

2   Click **Fill Icon**. Select and click desired colour.

3   Double Click on the quadrant.
Select **Size**.
Rotation: Insert 45.

4   Click on quadrant.
Copy & Paste.

5   Click on new quadrant.
Click on **Draw**.
Rotate Left.
Copy & Paste.

6   Click on new quadrant.
Click on **Draw**.
Rotate Left.
Copy & Paste.

7   Click on new quadrant.
Click on **Draw**.
Rotate right until you get the desired positioning.

8   Align the quadrants together.
Use the ZOOM to enlarge. This wll help you to align the shapes

9   Click on **Autoshapes**.
Basic Shapes
Rectangle. Hold **Shift** key to create a square. Double click on square.
Select **Size**.
Rotation: Insert 45.

10   Move square to the 4 aligned quadrants.
Click **Fill Icon**. Click **No Fill**.
Click **Draw**, **Order** and **Send to Back**.

9. To make a fraction table

1 Click **Table**

2 Click **Insert Table**

Number of rows : 10
Number of columns : 1

3 Click **OK**. A table will be drawn. Use the mouse to move over the second row.

4 Click or highlight the second row

5 Click **Table**

6 Click **Split Cells**

Number of columns : 2 (to divide the whole into 2 parts) Put in the number of parts you want.

- Do the same for the rest of the rows. Highlight the row, then go to **Table** (pull down menu). Click **Split cells** and indicate the desired number of columns.

One whole							
$\frac{1}{2}$				$\frac{1}{2}$			
$\frac{1}{4}$		$\frac{1}{4}$		$\frac{1}{4}$		$\frac{1}{4}$	
$\frac{1}{8}$	$\frac{1}{8}$	$\frac{1}{8}$	$\frac{1}{8}$	$\frac{1}{8}$	$\frac{1}{8}$	$\frac{1}{8}$	$\frac{1}{8}$

One whole											
$\frac{1}{3}$				$\frac{1}{3}$				$\frac{1}{3}$			
$\frac{1}{6}$		$\frac{1}{6}$		$\frac{1}{6}$		$\frac{1}{6}$		$\frac{1}{6}$		$\frac{1}{6}$	
$\frac{1}{12}$	$\frac{1}{12}$	$\frac{1}{12}$	$\frac{1}{12}$	$\frac{1}{12}$	$\frac{1}{12}$	$\frac{1}{12}$	$\frac{1}{12}$	$\frac{1}{12}$	$\frac{1}{12}$	$\frac{1}{12}$	$\frac{1}{12}$
$\frac{1}{2}$						$\frac{1}{2}$					

One whole									
$\frac{1}{5}$		$\frac{1}{5}$		$\frac{1}{5}$		$\frac{1}{5}$		$\frac{1}{5}$	
$\frac{1}{10}$	$\frac{1}{10}$	$\frac{1}{10}$	$\frac{1}{10}$	$\frac{1}{10}$	$\frac{1}{10}$	$\frac{1}{10}$	$\frac{1}{10}$	$\frac{1}{10}$	$\frac{1}{10}$
$\frac{1}{2}$					$\frac{1}{2}$				

10. To draw a pie chart

1 Click the Excel icon on the standard toolbar.

A Data sheet like the one below will be shown.

2 Place the cursor at the first cell on the first column. Click the cell. All the cells will be highlighted.

		A	B	C	D	E
		1st Qtr	2nd Qtr	3rd Qtr	4th Qtr	
1	East	20.4	27.4	90	20.4	
2	West	30.6	38.6	34.6	31.6	
3	North	45.9	46.9	45	43.9	
4						

E:\Bank\1-TN\Fractioncity.... - Datasheet

3 Click **Edit**
Click **Clear**
Click **All**
(The above three steps will clear all data that is given in default.)

4 Place the cursor at the first cell on the first column again.

5 Click **Chart**
Click **Chart Type**

Click **Pie**
Click the first chart sub-type as shown.

Click **OK**

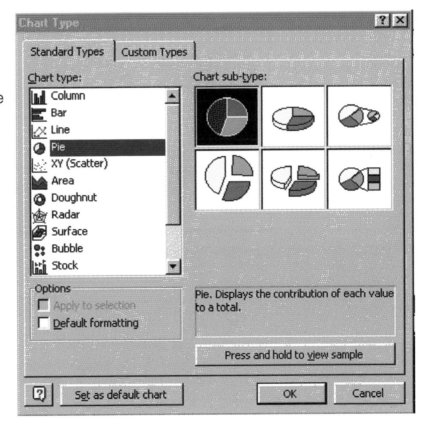

151

Click **Data**
Click **Series in Column**

6 At the second column and second cell, key in the value "1".
Do the same for the next 2 cells.

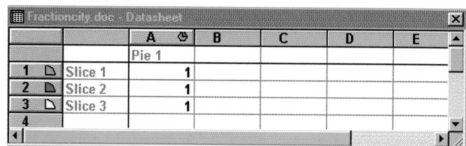

The chart shown
will be a circle
that is divided into
three equal parts.
Add more slices
to the chart if more equal parts are required.

To change the colour of the background

1 Double click the pie chart to edit it.

2 Click the data sheet and move it away from the pie chart.

3 Move the cursor to the pie chart to the top right part of the pie chart and right click.

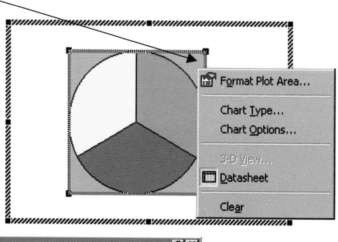

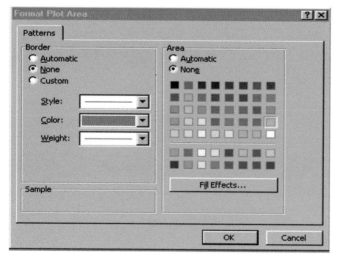

Another menu panel will pop up as shown.

4 Left click **Format Plot Area**.

5 Click **None for Border**.
Click **None for Area**.

6 Click **OK**.
(These steps will take away the border and background of the pie chart).

To change the colour of a part of a pie chart

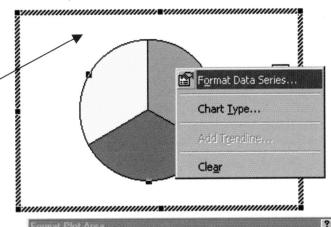

| 1 | Move the cursor over the pie chart until you get the handles of the pie chart on the outside. |

| 2 | Right click the mouse to get the pop up menu. |

Left click **Format Data Series**. to get the pop up menu for the plot area.

Click **Area none** to get no colour. Leave the border as you will need it to show the difference between the parts of the pie chart.

Click **OK**.

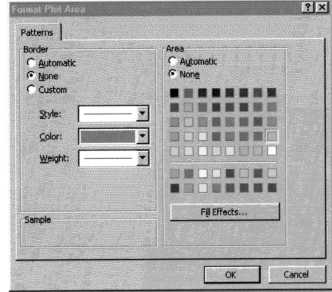

To change individual parts of the pie chart

- Move the cursor to the desired part and click until the handles of the pie chart surrounds the part whose colour you want changed.

To delete the legend of the pie chart

- Move the cursor to the legend and click until the handles surrounding the legend appear. Then press **Delete**.

Lesson plans on computer-based learning

Here are some examples of IT lesson plans for the teaching of Mathematics using available software and the teachers' creativity. Relevant worksheets are also attached. (For further examples, please refer to the CPDD website in the MOE's intranet page.)

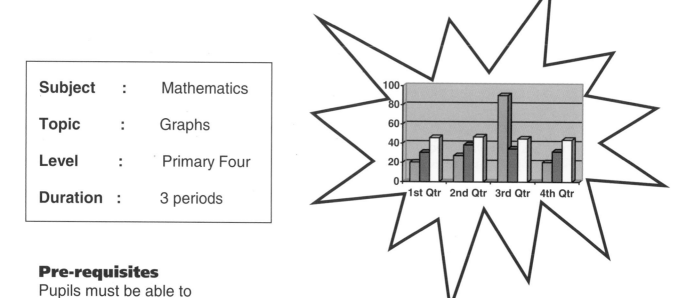

Subject	:	Mathematics
Topic	:	Graphs
Level	:	Primary Four
Duration	:	3 periods

Pre-requisites
Pupils must be able to
- complete a table from given information.
- read and interpret tables.

Specific Instructional Objectives
Pupils should be able to
- create a bar graph with given data.
- read and interpret bar graphs and tables.

Thinking skill
- Gathering and organising data

Learning and teaching materials
1. Courseware: *The Graph Club*
2. Workbook: Primary Mathematics 4A (Exercise 39 to 43)
3. Worksheets 1 - 4
4. Fruit Cards: 44 (Mangosteen: 9, Durian: 16, Apple: 8, Papaya: 11)

Learning Environment
- Half of the computer laboratory

Instructional Strategies

1. Pre-lesson activity:
   (a) Divide class into 4 groups.
   (b) Assign each group to collect one set of data using Worksheets 1 to 4.
   (Examples of data include number of siblings, mode of transport, month of birth and types of residence.)

2. Show the class how data can be represented in the form of picture and bar graphs using the **Explore** mode of the courseware *The Graph Club.* Change some data in the picture graph and elicit response from pupils about the corresponding changes in the bar graph. Highlight to pupils how the graphs are related.

3. Show pupils how data can be organised.
   (a) Distribute the fruit cards.
   (b) Tally the number of pupils with different kinds of fruit cards (Mangosteen, Durian, Apple and Papaya)
   (c) Tabulate the data collected using the courseware *The Graph Club.*
   (d) Generate a bar graph based on the data in (c).

4. Get pupils to work in pairs to tabulate the data which they have been assigned to collect before the lesson. Pupils are to also generate the corresponding bar graph using the **Create** mode of *The Graph Club.*

5. Get pupils to present their graphs to the class. Elicit from pupils the highest and lowest values for each category from the graphs.

6. Pupils are to do Exercise 39 to 43 in Workbook 4A.

Worksheet 1

Graphs (mode of transport)

Names of group members: **Class:** _____

(1)_____   **Date:** _____

(2)_____

(3)_____

(4)_____

Mode of transport	Number of pupils
Car	
MRT	
School bus	
Walking	

Worksheet 2

Graphs (Number of siblings)

Names of group members: **Class:** _____

(1)_____   **Date:** _____

(2)_____

(3)_____

(4)_____

Number of siblings	Number of pupils
0	
1	
2	
3 or more	

Worksheet 3

Graphs (month of birth)

Names of group members: **Class:** _____

(1)_____   **Date:** _____

(2)_____

(3)_____

(4)_____

Month of birth	Number of pupils
January – March	
April – June	
July – September	
October – December	

Worksheet 4

Graphs (types of residence)

Names of group members:

(1)_____

(2)_____

(3)_____

(4)_____

Class: _____

Date: _____

Types of residence	Number of pupils
3 – 4 room HDB flat	
5-room HDB flat	
Private condominium	
Private house	

Subject	:	Mathematics
Topic	:	Average
Level	:	Primary Five (EM 1/2)
Duration	:	2 periods

Pre-requisite
Pupils must be able to
- use the features in *The Cruncher.*
- find average.

Specific Instructional Objectives
Pupils should be able to
- find the average pulse rate.
- read and interpret data.

Thinking skill
- Comparison

Learning and teaching materials
1. Courseware: *The Cruncher*
2. File named <average.mtk> (See **Annex 1** for its preparation.)
3. Stopwatch

Learning environment
- Classroom with 10 multimedia notebooks (fully charged)
- Field

Instructional strategies
1. Consolidate the concept of average by starting with the familiar, for example, money. Get pupils to act out the scenario: 5 pupils take out their money and record the individual amounts. Then they put the money together and distribute it equally. From here, elicit from pupils the formula for calculating average, which in this case is what each pupils gets after the distribution.

2. This formula is then used in the following activities. Tell pupils that they are given 30 minutes to find the average pulse rate of a normal child for different activities such as walking, jogging, etc.
   a) Demonstrate how pulse rate can be taken at the wrist.
   b) Brief pupils how to carry out the activity. Show them how to record the pulse rate using the file named <average.mtk>.
   c) Divide pupils into groups of 4 and instruct them to carry out their activities in the school field. Remind them to record the pulse rate into the file <average.mtk>.

3. At the end of 30 minutes, get pupils to present their findings on the average pulse rate of a normal child for all the activities stated. Pupils are to compare the average pulse rates of boys and girls and the average pulse rate for different activities.

(Worksheet 1)

Procedure for the preparation of the diskettes containing file <average.mtk>.

	A	B	C	D	E
1					
2		Names of pupils			
3	Activities				
4	At rest				
5	Walking for 1 min				
6	Running for 1 min				
7	Running for 2 min				

section 7

Annexes

Name: _____( ) Class: Pr_____ Date: _____

FRACTIONS

1. If this bar is a whole, shade $\frac{1}{4}$ of it.

2. If this bar is $\frac{1}{3}$ of a whole, complete the whole bar.

3. If this bar represents 1 whole, complete $1\frac{1}{2}$ bars.

4. If this bar represents $1\frac{1}{2}$, shade 1 whole.

5.

(a) Colour $\frac{4}{7}$ of the bar (above) red.

(b) The fraction left would then be _____.

(c) Now, colour another $\frac{2}{7}$ of it blue.

(d) The fraction of the bar that is left with no colour is _____.

Name: _____( ) Class: Pr_____ Date: _____

FRACTIONS

1.

(a) Shade $\frac{1}{5}$ of the bar blue.

(b) The fraction that is now left uncoloured is _____.

(c) Colour $\frac{1}{2}$ of the remainder red.

(d) The fraction of the bar that is coloured red is _____.

(e) The fraction of the bar that is <u>not</u> coloured at all is _____.

2.

(a) Colour $\frac{1}{5}$ of the bar blue.

(b) Colour $\frac{1}{4}$ of the bar red.

(c) The fraction of the bar that is <u>not</u> coloured is _____.

3.

(a) Colour $\frac{1}{5}$ of the bar blue.

(b) Colour $\frac{1}{4}$ of the remainder red.

(c) The fraction of the bar that is <u>not</u> coloured is _____.

4.

(a) Colour $\frac{2}{5}$ of the bar blue.

(b) Colour $\frac{1}{4}$ of the remainder red.

(c) The fraction left uncoloured is _____.

Name: _____( ) Class: Pr____ Date: _____

FRACTIONS — PROBLEM SUMS

Try using models to solve the following sums.

1. There are 340 toy dogs and cats. $\frac{2}{5}$ of the toy dogs is equal to $\frac{4}{7}$ of the toy cats. How many toy dogs and how many toy cats are there?

2. There are 990 apples and oranges at the stall. If $\frac{2}{3}$ of the apples is equal to $\frac{4}{9}$ of the oranges, how many more oranges are there than apples?

3. $\frac{3}{4}$ of Jack's monthly allowance is equal to $\frac{1}{2}$ of Benny's monthly allowance. After Benny had spent $100, he found that he had the same amount as Jack's monthly allowance. How much was Jack's monthly allowance?

4. $\frac{3}{5}$ of Class A and $\frac{3}{4}$ of Class B are girls. Both classes have the same number of girls and Class A has 8 more boys than Class B. How many pupils are there in Class A?

5. Ali and Bob together had $150. After Ali had spent $56 and Bob had spent $20, $\frac{2}{5}$ of Ali's remainder is equal to $\frac{5}{6}$ of Bob's remainder. How much did Ali have at first?

6. Of the 230 eggs Mrs Lee bought, $\frac{3}{4}$ of the number of large ones is the same as $\frac{2}{5}$ of the number of smaller ones. If he sold the eggs as stated below, how much would he get if he sold them all?

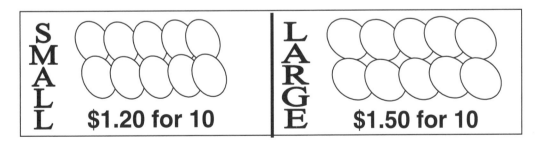

SMALL $1.20 for 10   LARGE $1.50 for 10

Name of Pupil: _____( )Class: Pr _____ Date:_____

MASS

1.(a)

	Describe the object e.g. orange, pencil, etc.
Object A	
Object B	
Object C	
Object D	
Object E	

Estimation of mass from lightest to heaviest:

Object ( )	Object ( )	Object ( )	Object ( )	Object ( )

(b)

Mass of Plasticine [   ] g/kg

Estimated mass of the objects:

Object ( )	Object ( )	Object ( )	Object ( )	Object ( )

(c) **Actual** mass of the objects:

Object ( )	Object ( )	Object ( )	Object ( )	Object ( )

How did you fare? Tick a box.

I am fairly accurate.	
I am accurate.	
I may need a little more practice.	

Remarks

Name: _____ ( ) Class: Pr ___ Date: _____

TRIANGLES AND THEIR RELATED RECTANGLES

1.(a) Draw a line, MN as shown in the diagram. M and N are both midpoints of AD and EF respectively.

(b) Cut out the 3 parts (P, Q and R) which are parts of the triangle lying outside Rectangle MNFD.

(c) Rotate these 3 parts to fit into the part MXD.

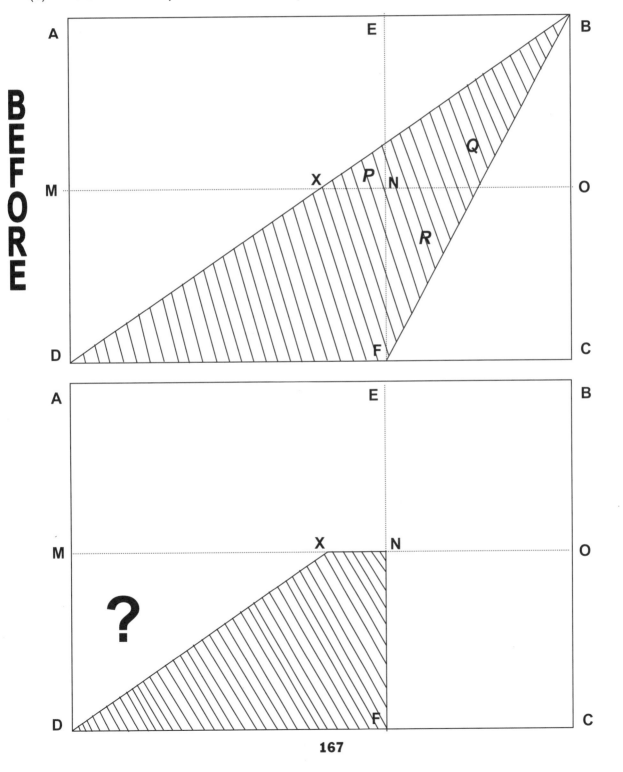

Continued ....

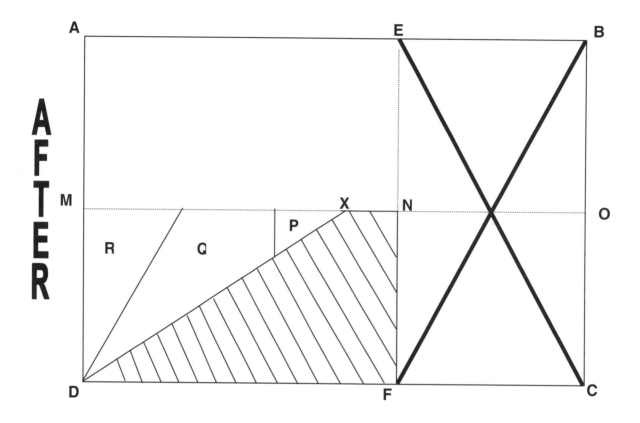

It can be seen that, the original Triangle BFD = $\frac{1}{2}$ Rectangle AEFD. Therefore AEFD is the related rectangle.

It has the same height and base as △ BFD.

Name: _____ (   ) Class: Pr ___ Date: _____

THE MEANING OF π

Radius = 3cm

Diameter = _____cm

Length of string around circle = _____cm

Length of string / Diameter ≈ [   ]

Radius = 4m

Diameter = _____cm

Length of string around circle = _____cm

Length of string / Diameter ≈ [   ]

This approximate figure is π.

So π is always about _____ times the diameter of a circle.

169

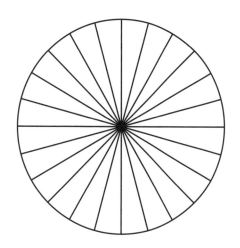

1. Colour and cut the circle as marked.
2. Make sure none of the strips is lost. (Hint: Cut into quarters first. Then cut from centre to side into the smaller strips.) Arrange all the cut parts on a line such that a rectangle is formed. (Hint: Arrange the parts by inverting them alternately.)
3. The radius would now be the breadth.
4. Measure the 'length' of this rectangle.
5. L × B would give you the area of the rectangle (which was a circle).
6. Using the formula for area of circles, compare the 2 answers.
7. Now you know how π helps us in solving the area of a circle!

✂----

Name: _____ (   ) Class: Pr_____ Date: _____

Area of Circles

Hands-0n-Activity: Arrange your 'circle strips' neatly along the line shown.

├───────────────────────────────────

Rectangle

Length (please measure) = _____cm

Breadth (radius of circle) = _____cm

Area of rectangle = _____ cm^2

Circle

$\pi = \dfrac{22}{7}$

Area = πr^2

Area = _____cm^2

Name: _____( ) Class: Pr _____ Date: _____

GEOMETRY — TESSELLATION

1. Put a tick where the shape can tessellate.

( )　　　　　　　( )　　　　　　　( )

( )　　　　　　　( )　　　　　　　( )

( )　　　　　　　( )　　　　　　　( )

( )　　　　　　　( )　　　　　　　( )

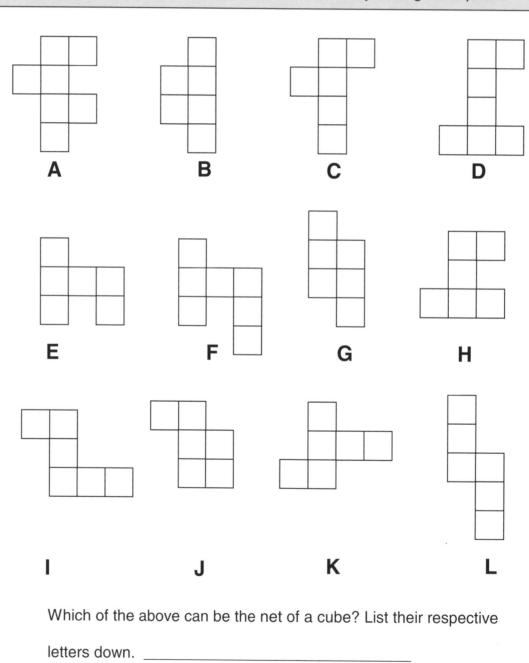

Name: _____ ( ) Class: Pr ___ Date: _____

GEOMETRY – NETS

1,   Which of the following nets are those of a cube?

Hint:
- Start by counting the number of squares. Do they tally with the number of faces that a cube has?
- Try to visualse whether a cube could be formed by folding the squares.

A   B   C   D

E   F   G   H

I   J   K   L

Which of the above can be the net of a cube? List their respective

letters down. _____

Name: _____( ) Class: Pr ___ Date: _____

GEOMETRY – NETS

1, Which of the following is the net of a cuboid?

Hint:
- Start by counting the number of shapes. Do they tally with the number of faces that a cuboid has?
- Compare the adjoining sides of the different shapes. Note their lengths.
- Think logically and find links to the various lengths.
- It is easier to focus on one shape as the base of the cuboid.

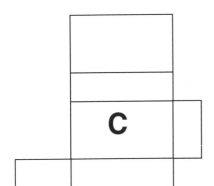

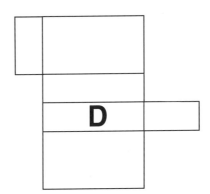

Name: _____(   ) Class: Pr ____ Date: _____

PERCENTAGE

1.

     A [| |]

     B [| | |]

     A is _____% of B.

     B is _____ % of A.

     A is _____ % less than B. (Remember what the base is.)

     B is _____ % more than A. (Remember what the base is.)

---

2.   May's pocket money is 20% less than June's. May has $80.
How much does June have?

     _____'s pocket money forms the base.

Fill in the correct names on these representations.

     (_____) [| | |]

     (_____) [| | | |]

     June has $_____.

TABLE OF SPECIFICATIONS

SECTION		(A) MULTIPLE-CHOICE				(B) SHORT-ANSWER				(C) PROBLEM SUMS				SUB-TOTAL
SKILLS	Relative weighting	No. of Qns	K	C	A	No. of Qns	K	C	A	No. of Qns	K	C	A	
TOPIC														

K: KNOWLEDGE
C: COMPREHENSION (UNDERSTANDING)
A: APPLICATION

number of qn per topic = $\dfrac{\text{Relative weighting of topic}}{\text{Total weighting}}$ × Total number of qn per section

Examples of questions assessing different cognitive levels

Topic	Knowledge	Comprehension	Application
Fractions	What is $\frac{1}{6}$ of 30 ?	Mary gave $\frac{5}{8}$ of her cake to her brother and $\frac{1}{3}$ of the remainder to her sister. What fraction of the cake has she left?	Amy, Benny and Carol shared a sum of money. Amy's share was half of what Benny and Carol received. Benny's share was $\frac{4}{9}$ of the sum of money. Carol received $15 less than Amy. What fraction of the sum of money was Amy's share? What was the sum of money?
Area and perimeter	The figure shows an equilateral triangle. What is its perimeter? 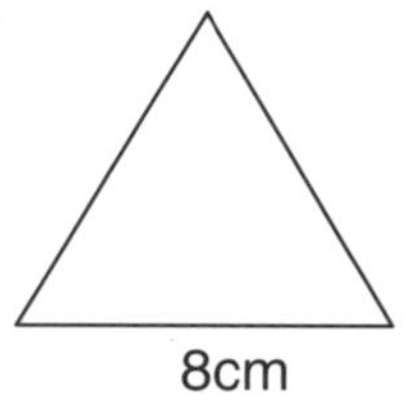 8cm	In the figure, what is the area of the shaded part? 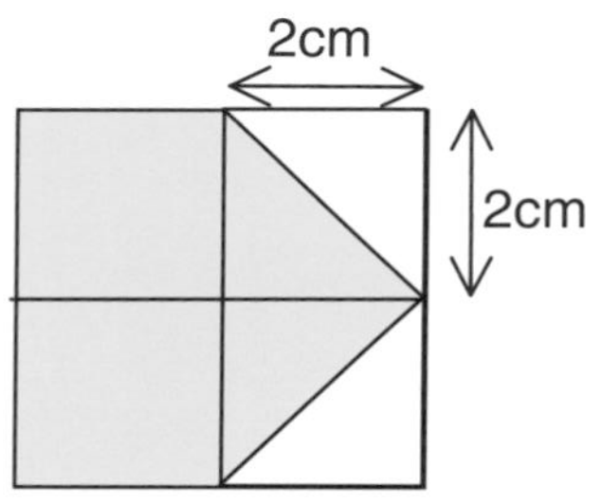 2cm 2cm	In the figure below, the shaded part is obtained by removing two semicircles of diameter 7 cm from a square of side 10 cm. Find the perimeter of the shaded part. (Take $\pi = \frac{22}{7}$ 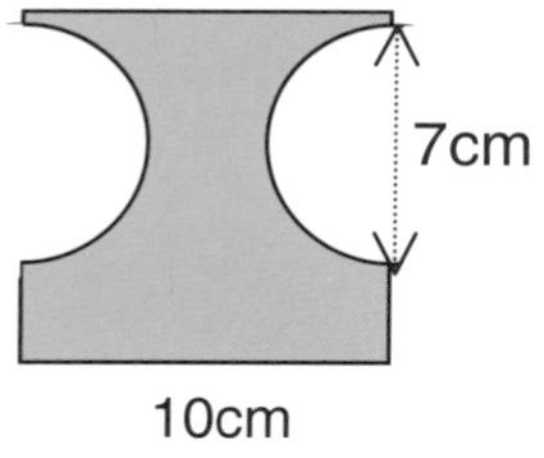) 10cm 7cm

Examples of non-routine/unfamiliar problems

The figure is made up of 4 squares A, B, C and D. What fraction of the figure is square C?	In the figure (not drawn to scale), find the value of $\angle a + \angle b + \angle c + \angle d$.	You are given a rectangular board and many identical triangular cards as shown below:
		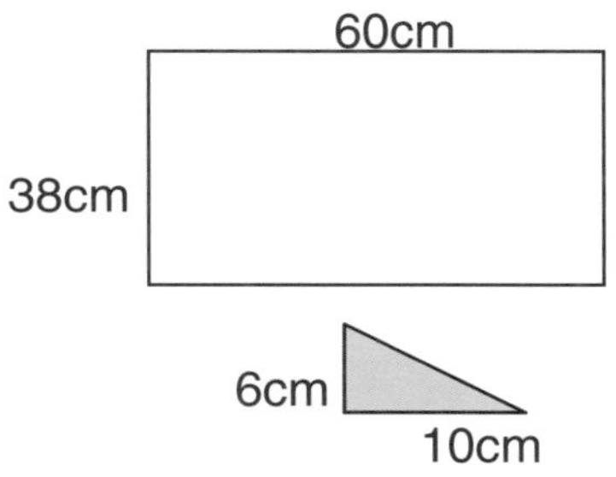 60cm
		38cm
		6cm 10cm
(Taken from 1999 PSLE paper)	(Taken from 1999 PSLE paper)	Use the cards to cover the board. You may not be able to cover the whole board. Without overlapping, what is the most number of cards you will need to cover the board as much as possible?
Answer: $\frac{1}{12}$	$125 + 125 = 250$ **Answer: 250°**	**Answer: 72**
How would you place 12 counters in 8 boxes so that there are 4 counters in each row and in each column? (Do not put any counters in the crossed section.)		May's age is a multiple of 3. Last year, her age was a multiple of 4. In 2 years' time, her age will be a multiple of 5. How old is she now?
Answer:		**Answer: 33 years**

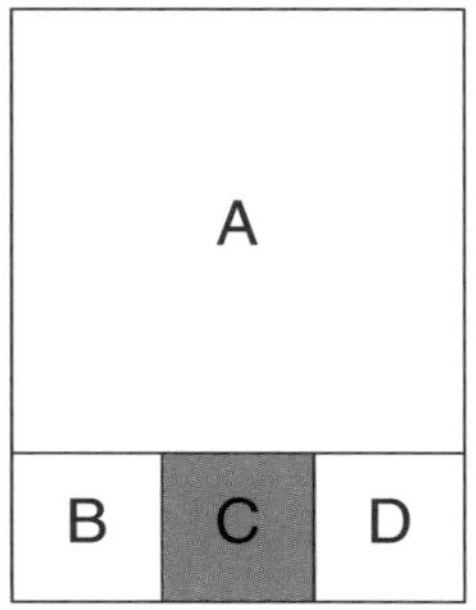

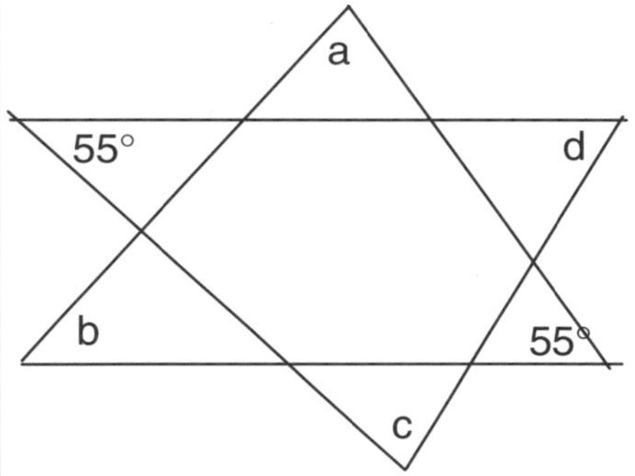

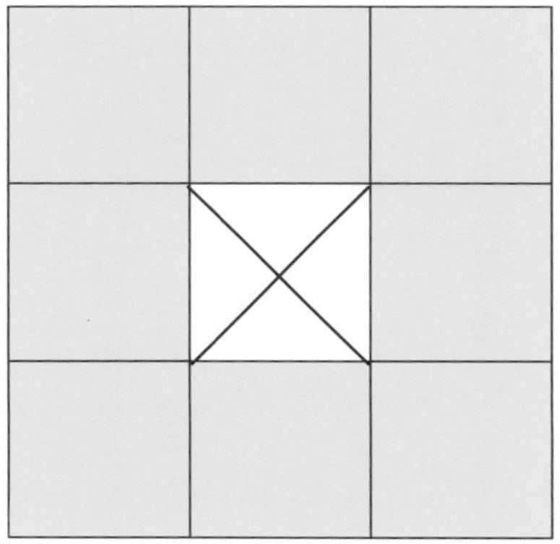

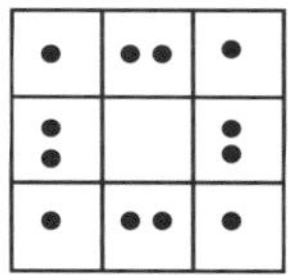

Acknowledgements

We would like to express our heartfelt appreciation to the following persons:

Mrs Kam Kum Wone, **DTD** (Director, Training Division)

Mr Nicholas Tang, **DDTN** (Deputy Director, Teachers' Network)

Mdm Fong Yuet Kwai, (Principal, Nan Hua Primary School)

Miss Ng Kin Yee (Jurong Institute) for her contributions, and most of all to

Miss Christina Cheong Ngan Peng

(NIE lecturer), for her advice and contributions.

References

1   Baker, Ann & Johnny (1991): <u>Counting on a small planet –</u>
<u>Activities for Environmental Mathematics</u>, Heinemann
Educational Books, Portsmouth, NH

2   Billstein, Rick (1987): <u>A Problem-solving Approach to Maths for</u>
<u>Elementary School Teachers</u>, 3rd ed., Benjamin/Cummings
Publications Co.

3   Curriculum Planning & Development Division, Sciences Branch,
Ministry of Education, Singapore (1993): <u>A Primary School's</u>
<u>Mathematics Programme</u>, 2nd ed.

4   Curriculum Planning & Development Division, Ministry of
Education, Singapore (2001): <u>Mathematics Syllabus Primary</u>

5   Ebel, Robert & Frisbie, David (1986): <u>Essentials of Educational</u>
<u>Measurement</u>, 4th ed., The Prentice-Hall, New Jersey

6   Ecker, Michael (1987): <u>Getting Started in Problem-solving and</u>
<u>Math Contests</u>, Franklin Watts

7   Kennedy, Leonard & Tipps, Steve (2000): <u>Guiding Children's</u>
<u>Learning of Mathematics</u>, 9th ed., Wadsworth Thomson Learning

8   Koay Phong Lee (1999): <u>Mathematics Activities for Upper</u>
<u>Primary Pupils</u>, Oxford University Press

9   Krulik, Stephen & Jesse Rudnick (1987): <u>Problem-solving –</u>
<u>A Handbook for Elementary School Teachers</u>, Allyn & Bacon

10   Kulm, Gerald (1994): <u>Mathematics Assessment</u>, Jossey-Bass
Inc., San Francisco

11   Lenchner, George (1983): <u>Creative Problem-solving in School</u>
<u>Mathematics</u>, Houghton Mifflin Co.

12   Lilburn, Pat & Rawson, Pam (1994): <u>Let's talk MATH –</u>
<u>Encouraging children to explore ideas</u>, Heinemann Educational
Books, Portsmouth, NH

13   O'Daffer, Phares ed. (1992): <u>Problem-solving: Tips for Teachers</u>
3rd ed., The National Council of Teachers of Mathematics, Inc.

14   Popham , James (1995): <u>Classroom Assessment: What Teachers</u>
<u>Need to Know</u>, Allyn & Bacon, Massachusetts

15   Van de Walle, John A. (1998): <u>Elementary and Middle School</u>
<u>Mathematics</u>, 3rd ed., Addison Wesley Longman Inc.

16   Wiersma, William & Jurs, Stephen (1990): <u>Educational</u>
<u>Measurement and Testing</u>, 2nd ed., Allyn & Bacon,
Massachusetts

NONRETURNABLE